Activity Planning
at Your
Fingertips

Note From the Author

Every now and then while researching, writing and preparing this book for publication, I became aware of a certain excitement dancing within my spirit. Something I had always dreamed of having during my nine years as an activity director was soon going to be a reality for others. Too often, the end of the month would creep up on me, and I'd be swamped with other responsibilities. I knew, though, that I still had to plan the next month's activity calendar. I liked doing it and wanted to try new and different things, but there wasn't always time. I longed to have all kinds of activity ideas right at my fingertips so I could just flip through a book and have my calendar planned in minutes. I never found that book.

Three years ago, I left the nursing home, and again became a full-time writer and publisher. I didn't need such a book anymore, yet I felt sure other activity directors did. Though I've written for *Family Circle, Christian Science Monitor, Women's Circle, True Story, Lady's Circle*, and numerous other magazines, I wanted to write for activity directors. Having known and dealt with thousands of them, I think activity directors are some of the best people in the world. It excited me to think other activity directors might be wishing for the same book. Consequently, *Activity Planning at Your Fingertips* was born.

I'm sure you have many great activity ideas that I haven't even touched on, and without a doubt, another book could well be written just to assemble them. Still, it is my desire that *Activity Planning at Your Fingertips* will make your professional calendar planning a whole lot easier. I pray it will meet your needs and that you will truly be blessed by it.

Please feel free to write me through Valley Press. I'd love to hear from you—to have you share your likes and dislikes, your ideas and your needs for professional material. I am here to serve.

Happy Activity Directing!

Marge

Activity Planning at Your Fingertips

by **Marge Knoth**

Valley Press
Bradenton, Florida
valleypressbooks@tampabay.rr.com

Printed by
United Graphic
Mattoon, Illinois

Eighth printing: February, 2008
Seventh printing: November, 2003
Sixth printing: March, 2000
Fifth printing: August, 1997
Fourth printing: February, 1995
Third printing: January, 1993
Second printing: November, 1991
First printing: September, 1990

Disclaimer

The ideas in this book are shared to help you offer your residents a full and interesting activity program. They are not, however, meant to be a fool-proof plan and must be used at your own risk. The author and publisher can take no responsibility for any failure or harm resulting from using the ideas, activities, projects, or any of the materials presented in this book.

ISBN: 0-927935-08-2

Table of Contents

Dedication

To Jesus, my Savior and Lord, who was at my side throughout my years at the nursing home, guiding me, leading me, using me...who's shared my joys and my tears; my victories and my frustrations; my successes and my failures; who loves me in spite of myself...and still reigns in my heart and guides me as I write. May He be glorified in this book and in my life.

The Challenge of
Activity Planning

Planning activities is a full time job. Offering just a mediocre program would wear out an ordinary person, but activity directors are made of better stuff. They are seldom content with run-of-the mill programs for their residents. They love them and want to meet their needs be they physical, emotional, mental or spiritual.

Often, though, when the end of the month rolls around and responsibilities have mounted, they find themselves with little time to sit down and plan a really fun-filled calendar. Consequently they are tempted to fall back on the tried and true: bingo, Bible study, movies, crafts and kitchen band. These are worthy activities and should be included in every calendar, yet a first-rate activity program should include so much more.

Calendar planning should not be a chore simply to endure; it should be a fun time for the activity director—a time when she can reflect and examine the needs of residents and then seek to meet them with specific activities. To adequately accomplish this task, though, the A.D. must allow desk time where he or she can quietly plan and chart. *Activity Planning at Your Fingertips* offers you two full years of pre-planned calendars, and in these calendars you'll notice that we have left Friday mornings free for this purpose. Don't feel guilty not offering constant activity or for spending a few hours in your office rather than on the floor. This is as much a part of your job as carrying out activities. In facilities where there are several on the activity staff, it may possibly be easier to get desk time, but in a one-activity director facility, it's a challenge. Yet, if you want a superior activity program, do yourself a favor and schedule time for *you* as well as for the residents.

Activity Planning at Your Fingertips is designed to let you plan a unique calendar each month in just minutes. More than 650 activity ideas are presented. Choose the type of activity you desire, look down the tabs to locate that category, turn to it and simply select one you like.

For those months when you simply don't have time to plan a calendar, use our pre-planned ones. Though this book is copyrighted and not to be reproduced in any way, you *do* have our permission to copy and use the calendars as you wish. Simply modify them to meet your personal needs.

Besides just planning and carrying out activities for your residents, a professional activity director seeks to bring positive press coverage to his or her facility. One way of doing that is by involving your community in your activities. You'll find several successful community outreaches in *Activity Planning at Your Fingertips*.

Activity directing is a unique profession which affords you constant challenges. And you can meet those challenges because you *are* an activity director. The Good Lord seems to have built into activity directors creativeness, unlimited energy and soft hearts. *Activity Directing at Your Fingertips* is just one more tool to help you be the professional activity director that you really are.

Planning
The Activity Calendar

Excerpt from *The Professional Activity Director*

Calendar planning doesn't have to be complicated. Here's a system that will take a lot of the frustration out of the process. There are some things that must go on your calendar year after year, month after month, week after week and day after day. So you won't forget any of these when you begin to plan, make yourself a master list.

Take a sheet of typing paper and turn it sideways. Write "Master Planning Sheet" at the top. Then rule off seven columns. Title the columns: *Daily, Weekly, Monthly, Yearly, Occasionally, Seasonally*, and *New Ideas*. Under both *Occasionally* and *Seasonally*, list the subtitles *Projects* and *Community Involvement*. These two subtitles are just tickler reminders to you.

Now let's take them, one at a time, and complete the master sheet beginning with *Seasonally* and working backwards to *Daily*. Under *Seasonally*, list all the holidays your facility celebrates: New Years, Presidents' Day, Groundhog Day, Valentine's Day, St. Patrick's Day, Easter, Father's Day, Mother's Day, Memorial Day, Independence Day, Labor Day, Columbus Day, Grandparents' Day, Thanksgiving, Election Day, Yom Kippur, Hanukkah, Christmas and any others you choose.

Now take a brand new yearly planning calendar, and at the top of each month, make a note of the holidays you wish to celebrate during that month. It's too early to select an actual date a year ahead, but when you come to planning activities for that particular month, your note will be there to remind you. Under *Seasonally*, as a community involvement, you might list a community Easter egg hunt at your facility, a Christmas party for underprivileged children or breaking green beans for the community.

Next, under the heading of *Yearly*, list the activities your facility likes to hold annually. Try to create some new ones. These might include: a pet show, fishing trip, Oktoberfest, hatching chicks, nursing home olympics, a trip to the park or a family cook-out. Now, go through your yearly planning calendar and make a note of your chosen annual activities in the months you want to hold them.

On your master planning sheet, look now to the *Occasionally* column. Under this heading, chart activities that take place two, three or more times a year. Here, you might want to write: baby-loving days, square dancers and bands. As a community outreach, you might list a celebrity day or a Walt Disney movie at your facility for kids of the community. Now, again go through your yearly planning calendar, and note these events at the top of the proper month.

Next, go to the *Monthly* column. This becomes easier because we are more familiar with our regular events. Here on your master sheet, list such things as: resident council, birthday parties, cooking, school class visits, basketball games and clubs that meet monthly. There's no need to transfer these yet to your planning calendar, as you can do that when you actually plan that month's activities. They'll be right there on your master sheet to remind you.

Look now at the *Weekly* column. Fill in such things here as: Bible study, bingo, movies and ceramics. Again, when you're planning the current month's activities, just transfer these events from your master sheet to the present month.

In the *Daily* column list: devotional, coffee group, word games, exercise—whatever you do daily. This list on your master sheet will keep the activities readily available to transfer when you are actually planning your calendar.

Under *New Ideas*, list activities you would like to try sometime. These might include community events, a luau, Christmas in July, doll show, making a quilt, a mock wedding or inviting a college coach and his team in to play basketball with your residents—nursing home style, of course. Each month when you plan your calendar, try to select at least one new idea to try. This keeps residents, staff and families watching your calendar to see what's coming next.

There you have a master sheet, the outline of a full year's calendar to be tacked prominently over your desk or stored with your planning calendar. Using this outline, along with *Activity Planning at Your Fingertips*, will make your calendar planning simple and quick. (See master sheet, Reference.)

How to Use Our
Pre-Planned Calendars

Facilities differ in the size of their activity departments and the number of activities required. These calendars, though they can easily be used by any size activity staff, have been planned so that a single activity director will easily be able to use them.

Monday and Wednesday mornings from 9-11 have been set aside for bedside activities. You will find many bedside activities listed as well as activities for low-functioning residents.

Tuesday morning has been reserved for a weekly *Do You Remember* coffee and donuts group. This group is designed to meet the needs of current events under the guise of a reminiscent activity. You may have to change the name to suit the requirements of your facility, but in effect, it will be the same group. Generally speaking, residents are more apt to come to a *Do You Remember* group than a *Current Events* group. They fear being embarrassed in a *Current Events* group because they have not been able to keep up with current happenings. You may wish to simply call your group *Coffee and Donuts* in order to satisfy everyone. A good reminiscence group begins with the residents looking back on a given subject or subjects and after their memories are discussed at length, being gently brought back to the present by discussing how things have changed and how they are done today. (See *Any Day*, reminiscence.)

Monday, Wednesday and Friday features 15 minutes of exercise while residents are in the dining room waiting to be served lunch. Tuesday and Thursday, during this same time, word games are offered. Some are listed specifically on the pre-planned calendars, but many others are offered in *Activity Planning at Your Fingertips*. (See *Word Games*.)

Mondays feature various facility clubs that are open to any resident who wishes to participate. Though it's not always possible to hold them on a specific Monday each month, an effort is made in that direction. We've tried to set aside, as much as possible, the first Monday for a sewing club, the second for a horticulture club and the third for a hospitality club. A history club is held on one Thursday, and a literary club and a men's club wherever there's a free calendar day. Beauty club is for those ladies who are very low-functioning and are not able to take part in many other activities. Thursday mornings have been set aside to fuss over these ladies, perhaps by brushing their hair, putting a pretty scarf on them or painting their nails. These clubs are optional, but they do serve to fill needs of residents who like specific activities.

Thursday afternoons feature a Catholic mass along with an additional (usually simple) activity. Sunday offers a Protestant service. You may want to occasionally have a Protestant Communion service perhaps on Good Friday. Residents' rhythm band usually takes place the first Friday of each month, though it gives way when needed. Crafts are generally scheduled the first Tuesday of each month and cooking is the second Tuesday. Since residents love their bingo, this is a regularly scheduled activity for Wednesdays, and we try hard not to change its day.

We've sought to hold a resident council meeting each month, one outing and a birthday party which is sometimes combined with another activity such as a clown visit or an ice cream social. A basketball game is held nearly every month with another facility or a school class, or sometimes it's just an in-house game.

Devotions may be held daily or as often as desired, if your facility doesn't object. A good time to hold a devotional is just before lunch, after exercises or word games. Little prepared booklets like *The Upper Room* or *God's Word For Today* (See *Reference* for address) frequently are donated to nursing homes. If not, check with churches or a Christian bookstore. They are dated, and each day offers a short reading and a scripture. You will need only one of these booklets. Residents like to listen to this short devotional that you or a volunteer can read. Then, since residents come from many different faiths, I have found it helpful, rather than a meal prayer, to simply have them recite *The Lord's Prayer* together. It seems to be one they all know.

Some states require two evening activities a week. This is difficult when a single A.D. is responsible for all activities. Since he or she can't function both night and day, we've planned most weekend and evening activities so his or her presence is not required. They can often be carried out by another department. For instance: a kindly nurse's aide can put on a movie for residents at a given time and rewind it when it's over. If you have a supportive kitchen staff, one night a week after they've cleaned up from the evening meal and are preparing to go home, they may well serve wine and cheese chunks (that you have purchased and cut up) to residents. Social hour can be achieved by someone gathering the residents together for a time of socializing. You may want to have magazines or photo books on hand for them to enjoy and a glass of juice.

For weekend activities, appoint an alert resident/volunteer to see that cards and games such as dominoes and checkers are put out at the proper time. Before you leave on week-ends, set up a card table with a partially finished jigsaw puzzle. Residents and their families can work on this together. Purchase tapes of old-time radio shows like *Jack Benny* or *The Shadow Knows* as well as songs of the 20's and 30's and 40's. Put a resident or volunteer in charge of playing these tapes at the proper time. Appoint alert residents or volunteers to supervise plant care, and let them know what you want done with the plants. Arrange for coffee and donuts to be served in your absence. Movies are always a good stand-by. Don't overlook sports on T.V. as a viable activity. Break out *Tinkertoys* and *Lincoln Logs,* and let residents have a contest who can build the best log cabin or truck or toy. Ladies may enjoy playing Jacks on the table. Try to arrange for guests who are comfortable coming to your facility in your absence to visit evenings or week-ends and offer simple activities to residents. This could include visits, singing or Scripture reading to interested residents.

These activities may or may not satisfy the requirements of your State Board of Health. I personally used them in Indiana for nine years, and they were acceptable to all state surveyors during that time.

In planning these calendars, we have sought to plan one big activity or project each month to give residents and the facility or the community something to look forward to. With the remaining days, we have chosen activities to include games, guests and other fun activities.

We certainly do not claim to have all the answers and all the activities, but we have sought to put under one cover a variety of activities that will simplify your calendar planning and perhaps offer you some new ideas to put a little more excitement in the hearts of your residents.

Activities for Bedside
and
Low-Functioning Residents

Activities for Bedside
and
Low-Functioning Residents

Chapter 1

Activities for Bedside
and Low-Functioning Residents

Entertaining bed patients is not always an easy task because there are so many variables. But you, the activity director, are challenged to see that no resident is without some type of activity. Here are a few you might try.

BASKETBALL: Even very confused residents can enjoy bucket basketball. Use a large cardboard container or a plastic waste basket, weighted in the bottom, and encourage residents to throw the ball into it. Cheer them when they make it, encourage them when they miss. You can take the bucket to bedside residents (if they are not too sick) and hold it up so they can try to shoot.

BEAN BAG TOSS: Gather several boxes or buckets and attach a point value to each. Place them at different distances from the resident. Let the resident toss bean bags into them. Cheer them on.

BOOK MAKING: It's sometimes difficult to find activities for the patient who's in the latter stages of Alzheimer's disease. You might try this. Go through magazines with them and note if something catches their attention. If it's babies, for instance, help them locate as many babies as they can find and tear them out. Help them place the pictures in a plastic page photograph album. That is their particular book. Keep it handy so other staff members can give it to them when they need something to entertain themselves.

BUTTON, BUTTON: Fill a large, clear plastic peanut butter jar with buttons of all colors, shapes and sizes. Ladies may respond more to this than men. Empty some buttons out on the table or bed tray and let residents sort through them. Ask them to notice the many different kinds. Notice that some are sparkling. Notice the colors and the shapes. Ask how many square buttons they can find. Guess how many are in the jar. Ask if they remember collecting mussels to sell to button factories. Ask them to find the biggest button. Ask if they ever sewed and attached buttons.

CAR LOVERS: Most men really enjoy automobiles. Put pictures of old-time automobiles up in their rooms—also pictures of modern ones. (These can often be found on calendars. Check with your party goods store in December. They receive numerous sample calendars with all sorts of pictures, and they just toss them out. Ask them to toss them your way.) Change these pictures periodically. Bring in model cars or toy ones that belong to children you know. Discuss how cars have changed over the years. Ask about the first time residents drove automobiles. If you know someone who's an automobile lover and likes the elderly, invite him in to visit with your men bed patients.

CARDS: Take a deck of cards with you on rounds. Ask residents to tell you what each number is. Have them guess a card before you turn it over. Ask how many cards are in a deck. Find all the kings, the queens, the jacks. Build a small house with the cards. You might try games like old maid, hearts, crazy eights or solitaire with able residents.

CATCH: A large rubber playground ball or a nerf ball are great to throw around and play catch with low-functioning or bedside residents.

CHECKERS: This is an activity that many bedside residents can play. If the patient is confused, he might still want to push the checkers around the board or put red on red squares or black on black squares.

CHILDREN'S VISITS: Most elderly respond positively to children. When children visit your facility, see if they'd like to visit your bed and low-functioning patients as well as the alert. Perhaps they will sing a little song or read a short story to residents.

CIRCUS: Obviously bed patients can't go to the circus but you can bring a little part of it to them. Locate circus posters and hang them in their rooms. (If you have only one poster, it can be duplicated at a copy shop on a laser color copier for just a few dollars.) Perhaps you can locate a juggler who will come to the bedside and entertain. Park zoos will sometimes bring baby lions, monkeys or other circus animals to visit nursing homes. Talk about the great circus of the past. Discuss famous clowns like Emmett Kelly. Ask about the circus parade that always preceded the setting up of the circus. Talk about food treats at the circus such as lemonade, cotton candy and peppermint sticks. Ask about the various side shows at the circus: the fat man, the two headed lady, and the sword swallower. Locate books about the circus and look at them with your bed patient.

CLAY: Rolling clay and shaping it can be great exercise for stiff fingers as well as lots of fun. Work with residents individually or with a small group gathered around a table. Clay seems to be less messy though a little stiffer than play dough. Buy clay in the toy section of a store.

COIN FUN: It's fun to share coin collections with residents. Even if you are not a collector, residents who often don't handle their own funds will enjoy handling coins. Fill a jar with pennies, nickels, dimes, quarters and half dollars. Let residents sort them, stack them and count them. Ask them what they could buy with that amount of money. Ask if they ever saved coins. What did they buy with their collection? Ask where they hid their money long ago so no one could find it? Ask if they had money in the banks in the 30's when they failed and if they lost any.

COLOR SORTING: When you buy milk in the plastic gallon jugs, save the plastic caps. They come in various colors. When you have several of different colors, put them in a box and take them to low-functioning residents. Have them sort them according to color and then count them and put them all back in the box.

COLORING: Many residents—alert, confused, or mentally retarded--like to color. Sit down with them; you color one page of the color book while they color the opposite page. That way, they will feel less alone in doing an activity children enjoy.

CUTTING: Many residents like to cut. Some will need to be totally supervised doing this. Let them cut greeting cards, construction paper, pictures from magazines, newspaper or fabric. Unless the resident is extremely confused, it's best to make the work worthwhile, that is have a reason and a use for the thing they are cutting.

DRAWING: Some residents are artistic; some are not. Still, give it a try with your bed or low-functioning residents. Use a clipboard so they have a hard surface to press against as they draw. Sketch with them. Perhaps you can draw a circle and one eye of a face. Ask them to draw the other eye. You draw the nose and let them draw the mouth. Let them decide if the drawing is male or female. Ask them to add a moustache or earrings, whichever is needed. Begin a scene. Draw a horizon line. Ask them to make clouds. You add a lake. Ask them to draw a tree. You draw a flower. Have them draw a sun. Continue until the picture makes sense of some sort. Hang it in their room if they desire.

FARMERS: Many residents were farmers. In the spring time, visit their room and show them grains of corn or other crops. Let them feel the grain. Bring garden seeds and let them look over the packages. Tell them it's planting season. Bring along pictures of tractors plus old pictures of farming with horses. (You can get these in books at the library.) Ask them to tell you about their farm and just how they went about planting. As the season continues, bring in grain at various stages of growth—a stalk of corn at knee high, later a couple ears of fresh-picked corn. Bring wheat or some tobacco leaves. You might even carry in some good rich soil and let farmers get their hands in it once again. Since they can't go to the farm, bring the farm to them. Hang in their rooms pictures of fields laden with crops or of farmers at work.

FEEL BAG: In a paper bag, place common items including many that have distinct textures. You might include a cotton ball, sandpaper, a nut shell, a raisin, a piece of leather, velvet, corduroy and flannel—also a rubber ball, plastic worm, a small piece of clothesline rope, bark from a tree, a leaf, satin ribbon and newspaper. Add some other items such as clothespins, writing pen, tape, a screw, candle, small teddy bear and a spool of thread. Allow bed patients and low-functioning residents to feel but not look in the bag and then guess what each item is.

FOOTBALL: Gather residents in a circle and put a 12" rubber ball on the floor and let them kick it back and forth to one another. It's really quite simple, but even confused residents can take part and really enjoy it.

FOOTBALL 2: Let residents play with the small electronic football games. Stay with them and cheer them on.

GARDENING: Most people gardened in days gone by out of necessity, but many because they loved growing things. When it's about planting time, bring several packets of seeds to the resident's room and talk about each one. You might include various vegetables such as carrots, peas, green beans, beets, some onion sets, and a potato. Let them handle and look over the packets. Encourage them to tell you all they know about growing each plant. Pretend you know nothing to encourage conversation. Bring some flower pots to their room and let them plant a few vegetable seeds. Set the pot in their window and let the bed patient observe its growth. Regularly, check it with them. Keep a record of its planting and growing time. If there's space, a large bucket with a cherry tomato plant would be a nice addition to a resident's room. That way they could actually eat their home-grown produce.

For flower lovers, use the same plan but substitute packets of flowers for vegetables and let them enjoy lovely flowers on their window sill. This activity can be done in a small group with low-functioning or confused residents as well as with bed patients.

GREETING CARDS: Greeting cards come in all styles, colors and shapes. Residents enjoy sorting through them, cutting them, and pasting them in books. Depending on their level of functioning, residents can do the different activities with them. Keep a supply on hand and readily available should a patient need something to do. Just looking at them is a good activity for Alzheimer's residents.

GROCERY SHOPPING: How grocery shopping has changed today! Locate some old catalogs with prices of food in days gone by (check your library). Then bring in the grocery ads from your paper and compare the prices. Ask about various old-time brands they used: flour (Pillsbury), sugar (Arbuckle), laundry soaps (P & G and Star City), bar soap (Pine Tar), cereals (Quaker Oats), candy and spices.

Ask about coupons and specials offered on coffee and sugar. (They used to get coupons that they could save and buy merchandise. Often housewives bought their whole Christmas in this way.) Bring in some products and let them guess the price. An example might be a box of cloves priced at approximately $3.00 or a bar of soap costing nearly a dollar or an empty milk carton. They may be shocked at how prices have changed. It's wise to keep a supply of empty product containers in your storage area and record their prices to use for the game, *The Price is Right*.

HANDWRITING: Some residents have not used a pen for many years. I've found they are generally thrilled when asked for their signature on a voting ballot or voter's registration card. Take a lined paper to their room and ask them to practice writing their name. Then work on other letters of the alphabet. Over time, see if there is an improvement.

MAGAZINE VIEWING: Go through a magazine with a resident. Choose those most suited to what you think would have interested the resident when he or she was in his or her prime. Talk about the things you see. Ask questions about their past life based on what you see in the magazine. Maybe they were fishermen or hunters. Use sports magazines. Maybe they were homemakers. Try homemakers' magazines such as *Woman's Circle*. Encourage them to talk.

MARBLES: Men will no doubt appreciate this activity more than ladies as it was a very popular game when they were children. Fill a jar with all colored marbles. You might purchase these at garage sales or antique shops to get some really old marbles like residents remember. Take them to the bedside and let men sort through them. Ask them to tell you about games they used to play. Have them tell you about different size marbles and how they were used. Attach 1-inch tall sides to a large dough board or a piece of plywood to make a box. Roll the patient's bed to a sitting position and lay the box across the patient's lap. Play an improvised game of marbles with him.

MOVIES: If a VCR is available, show movies in the resident's room. Bring two or three ambulatory residents into a bed patient's room to watch the movie together. If their diets allow, serve popcorn and juice or a soft drink. Try to locate old time movies. Most residents enjoy Laurel and Hardy films where they can really laugh at their antics. Men might enjoy some of the gangster films made in the 30's and 40's. Women would usually prefer more romantic films. Seek those made between the 30's and 50's.

NEWSPAPER ROLLING: Use a large dowel rod or a sawed-off broom stick and show residents how to roll newspaper around it. When the rolls are made, remove the rod and tie a piece of bright yarn around them and give one to the resident.

NURSERY RHYMES: Most residents, alert or confused, enjoy hearing the old nursery rhymes they learned long ago. Get a book and read the first line and let them fill in the next line.

NUTS AND BOLTS: Bring a small plastic tool box to the bedside that has been filled with various sizes of nuts and bolts and washers. This works well with men who have been mechanics or worked with their hands using tools. Let them examine the box and put the nuts and washers on the bolts. Perhaps you can have a small block of wood enclosed in the box that has holes drilled in it so residents can fit the bolts through and secure them. Even confused residents would enjoy this one.

PAINTING: Sit at a table or at a bedside tray and paint with residents. You might choose to use color books for pictures, but it's fun to let them be creative with a paint brush and a blank sheet of paper. You might even experiment with finger painting with confused residents. Use a high-gloss paper and non-toxic finger paints. Other A.D.'s have used colored whipped cream and let residents finger paint with that. Save roll-on deodorant bottles. Pop the top out and fill them with tempera paint. Add about a tablespoon of oil per bottle. Push the roll-on ball back in. Let residents paint with these. This can be used at the bedside or working with confused individually or in small groups. Alert residents, too, can enjoy being creative with this new painting tool.

PAPER DOLLS: (See *Any Day.*)

PET VISITS: Pets will often get a response from a resident who takes part in nothing else. Dogs are especially welcome since most residents had a special dog at one time or another. Contact friends to bring their pets. Encourage staff to bring theirs, or call the animal shelter or local park zoo and ask if they'd bring animals to visit. Let residents hold them and pet them. Contact a farmer and ask to borrow baby chicks or ducks. He might even bring in a baby pig or lamb. Be sure to visit the former farmers'rooms with the farm animals.

PHOTO SHARING: Ask the family to bring in the resident's old photo albums and spend time going through them with him or her, asking lots of questions about who each person is. If the resident doesn't have a photo album from long ago, make him one. Start taking photos of the resident and of his guests. Add pictures cut from magazines that pertain to things that pique his or her interest—farming, pets, babies, food.

PRE-SCHOOLERS: This works best in small groups. Invite in a few low-functioning residents and an equal number of pre-schoolers. Provide toys and a box of old hats and dress up clothes. You might provide *Tinkertoys* or *Lincoln Logs*. Then just sit back and let residents watch the children. No doubt, they will soon become involved with them.

PUPPETS: You can buy hand puppets as simple or as nice as your budget allows. Some days make rounds with them on your hands. You're sure to bring a smile to residents. You might even find residents who won't open up to you baring their souls to the puppet.

READING: Some residents can read, but many cannot or are not interested. That's where you or a volunteer come in. Take a magazine that features the resident's interests to their room and go through it with them, looking at the various pictures. Read the captions with them. If the resident shows interest, ask if he or she would like you to read a little of the article to them. If a resident has a longer attention span, you might keep a book in his or her room and read a chapter a week. You might try some of the classic books of their childhood. *Guideposts* inspirational stories are great! Just the right length.

REMEMBER BOX: These boxes are not to be left with residents but to be used with your supervision only. Make a separate box for men and one for women. For men, fill a tool box with items they might remember—screwdriver, sandpaper, screws, key ring, leather wallet, coins, washers, fishing line, an Eversharp, and electrical tape.

For women, fill a large sewing box with items such as thread, tape measure, cookie cutters, spice cans, measuring cups, perfume bottle, clothes pin and a hankie. Set the box on a table or bed tray and let them take items out one at a time and tell you something about the use of that item from their past life.

REMINISCING: Use a good book designed for getting residents talking. (See *Any Day*).

RIBBON ROLLING: Try letting bed patients roll funeral ribbons around their fingers and secure them with paper clips for storage.

RIDDLES: Get a book of riddles and ask residents to guess them.

SCRAPBOOK: Buy an inexpensive photo album, if your budget allows. If not, make a scrapbook from left-over wallpaper. Punch holes in one side and secure with yarn. Help residents cut pictures from magazines and paste in their book. Also put in things that might interest them— party napkins, drawings from children or photographs. From time to time, help them add to their book. On other days just look at it with them and ask lots of questions.

SHOW AND TELL: At the bedside, look around the room and point out objects such as the painting on the wall, plants, vase, photographs, and ask the resident to tell you about each item—where they got it, what it means to them, the person who gave it to them.

SING-A-LONG: If you play a guitar this one is an easy activity. If not, locate someone who does and invite that person to come once a month or so and go to bed patients and play and sing a song or two for them. Choose songs they will remember like *Daisy, Daisy* or *I Want a Girl Just Like the Girl Who Married Dear Old Dad*. It doesn't have to be a guitar; other instruments could be used.

SOAP BUBBLES: Blow bubbles and watch residents respond. Let them try. Count the bubbles. Ask residents questions about bubbles. "What do they look like? Do they look like balls? Did you ever use bubble bath? When else do you see bubbles. Have you ever filled your dishwater with bubbles? Do you remember when your babies blew bubbles? Were soap bubbles available when you were a child? When did you first see soap bubbles? Is it fun to try something silly like this? How do you spell bubble." Encourage them to try again. No doubt you'll have lots of laughs.

SMELL BOX: Collect several scents and take them to residents' rooms and see how many they can identify. You might try cinnamon and other spices, vanilla, sawdust, lemon, kerosene (just emptied into a small bottle and then dumped out to leave the smell but cause no harm). Try to find as many scents as you can. Remember men and women might be more keen to identifying different smells that pertain to their past lives.

SORTING: As said before, residents can be given various items to sort by color, shape, size or use. Men might enjoy being given a box of nuts, bolts, and washers all mixed together. Ask them to separate them into three small jars.

SPECIAL GUESTS: Many interesting guests visit your facility to provide activities for the alert residents. You might ask the appropriate ones to give a few more minutes and visit two or three bed patients.

SPOOL FUN: Wooden spools, if you can get them (lots of people still have them around), are great for stringing. Use a bright colored round shoe string or yarn with Scotch tape wrapped around the ends for easy threading.

STAMP COLLECTING: A collection of stamps is easy to take to bedside residents who might be interested. Aside from just collector items, begin to watch your incoming mail. There is often an array of interesting stamps that residents would enjoy looking over. Christmas is an especially good time to find these since so much mail arrives at your facility. Alert your facility's secretary not to throw away unusual stamps.

TAPE LISTENING: Sometimes a resident is so sick that he or she is able to do nothing but listen to tapes. *Recordings for Recovery* (see References for address) supply tapes of any kind of music desired. They also offer sound tapes such as trains, water, wind. Residents enjoy music from the days when they were young, so seek that rather than just the local radio station's selection. *Guideposts*, a wonderful inspirational magazine, offers subscriptions on tape. Residents enjoy these. Ask their family members or friends to make tapes in which they talk to the resident. Play that tape for the resident when he or she is depressed. You might help them make a tape and then play it back so they can hear themselves on tape.

YARN WINDING: Some low-functioning residents and even bed patients can roll yarn into a ball. Encourage them.

Any Day Activities
❋
Games
❋
Exercise

Any Day Activities
*
Games
*
Exercise

Chapter 2

Any Day Activities

✓ANN LANDERS: A few weeks before this activity, begin to collect Ann Landers or Dear Abby columns from the newspaper. Gather residents together and read a letter written to the columnist. Don't read the answer. Ask residents, one by one, how they would solve the problem. Then read Ann Landers' or Abby's answer and discuss it. This is a form of current events since it orients residents to the changing modes of society.

(TRAVEL CLUB)

✓ARMCHAIR TRAVEL: Locate travel-type movies. *Modern Motion Pictures* have several on a free-loan basis. (See Reference for address.) When you choose a movie about a certain country, select snacks common in that country and serve them after the movie. For instance: Japan, egg rolls or won tons; Greece, rich pastries; Switzerland, cheese and crackers; England, tea and crumpets.

ART SHOW: Invite one or more local artists in to show their work and to tell a little about each piece. Perhaps they will create a picture or give a demonstration while residents look on.

You can invite an art museum to bring paintings and leave them on display for a day, or you can borrow some from your local library if they have a loan-a-painting program. Using this program, paintings are checked out like books.

BEAUTY MAKE OVER: This can be done in two ways. First, contact beauticians you know, or call salons and tell them of your desire to plan a special day for beauty make-overs for residents. Ask if they or a fellow beautician would donate one hour on a given afternoon to lift the spirits of senior citizens. They are usually happy to assist. Try to get beauticians or simply women who enjoy working with hair and nails. Beforehand, scrounge up hair dryers, extension cords, rollers, mirrors, make-up, and nail polish. Choose a workable number of female residents who would appreciate this, and let the beauticians get to work. Entertain the men with a cowboy movie during this time.

The second way is to use a class of school kids rather than beauticians. Sixth to eighth graders work well. They may not wash and set the ladies hair, but they can use curling irons and style it, and they can paint fingernails while visiting with residents. This should be good for a story in the newspaper or on T.V. Send out a press release a week before. If desired, this activity can be held the day before your facility is having a queen contest.

BRAGGING TIME: On a slow afternoon or when your regularly scheduled activity doesn't show up, schedule bragging time. Gather residents in a circle and ask who has the most grandchildren. Ask them to tell you about them. Also, ask if they remember when their children were young. Ask what was the cutest thing their child or a grandchild ever did. Ask them to tell you about the greatest accomplishment of their life. Inquire about their best friend and the nicest thing they ever did. Ask about their favorite pet. Inquire what these pets did that made them special. Determine whose pet was the smartest. Pets are a subject that will keep residents talking for a long time. Try to pull every resident into the discussion. Take notes. Put their pet stories in your newsletter.

BUILD A SNOW MAN: If you live in a part of the country that has snow, this is a really special and exciting activity. It will probably even bring the newspaper or television station in to feature your facility on the evening news. First, utilize some employees or volunteers to roll a big snow ball for the base. Bring this inside along with a wheelbarrow full of snow or several buckets full. Put a large plastic tablecloth on the floor and another one on a table. Around the tablecloth on the floor, gather residents who wish to help. Choose those who are ambulatory or who can maneuver their wheelchairs themselves. Put less able residents around the table. Provide everyone with gloves. Let the table people build a small snowman and the others a larger one. Don't forget to add a scarf, eyes, a carrot nose and a broom.

CAKE DECORATING: Perhaps your kitchen will bake you a couple sheet cakes. Short of this buy two inexpensive cakes. Make up powdered sugar frosting or buy the canned kind. Buy disposable decorating bags and plastic decorating tips, or borrow cloth bags and metal tips from someone who decorates cakes.

Color the frosting and fill the bags. Let residents practice on waxed paper or plastic lids that snap on coffee or shortening cans. After they have the knack, let residents decorate the cakesDon't forget candles and sprinkles. This activity can be the entertainment for residents' monthly birthday party, or it can be held the day before and the cake used for the party.

CURRENT EVENTS: Most facilities require that you have a current events group. Residents, on the other hand, soon become bored with current events. Somehow the discussion always seems to lead to "I remember when...," and your current events group is no longer a current events group but rather a reminiscence group. What can you do? As the old saying goes, "If you can't beat `em, join `em." Combine the two groups, and you'll have a much greater turnout for your activity. Call it a *Do You Remember?* group and let them talk about things of the past. Then gently bring them back to the present by discussing how things have changed and how they are done today. (See Reference for tools on leading a reminiscence group.)

GREEN THUMB DAY: If you find yourself with a cancellation on your activities for the day, here's a good one. Ask each resident who can, to bring from their room a plant or a flower arrangement. Artificial ones are fine. Display them all on a table and let residents look them over and identify the various kinds of plants. If they need work, this is a good time for residents to help each other pull off dead leaves or to water them. Residents may trade plants with one another if they wish. Encourage conversation about unique plants they have had in their lifetimes.

HAT FUN: Begin collecting hats: old-time ladies' hats, current ones, sailor hats, men's caps, nurses' caps, sock caps, fast-food restaurant hats, army helmets, foot ball helmets—any kind of hat you can find. Spend an activity period having everyone try on hats. Provide plenty of mirrors. Even the men enjoy trying on male-type hats.

MAKE PAPER AIRPLANES: Provide plenty of white typing paper and paper clips for weights. Invite a class of school kids over if you like. This makes your job easier. Have the kids help residents make paper airplanes and sail them. They will love this activity.

MAKE SNOW ICE CREAM: Dietary may be a little sticky on this because of the pollutants in today's air, but residents lived in a day when snow ice cream was a real treat. Locate clean snow and scrape off the top. Bring in a dish pan full.

To this, add some half and half or milk, sugar and vanilla. Mix. Serve immediately.

MEN'S PRETTY LEG CONTEST: The ladies have their beauty contests, but here's a chance for men to show off. Just tell the men you're having a beauty contest. They will all want to come not knowing they are the contestants. Select three ladies to be judges. Line the men across the front of the room and allow the women to sit in a semi-circle or anywhere to get a good view. Then ask the men, one at a time, to pull up their pants leg and let the judges decide who has the prettiest leg. This is a good activity because it allows the patients to laugh and have a good time.

MOVIES: Show a video or a 16 mm movie. Travel movies are always interesting. (See Reference for address of free movies.)

NAME THAT TUNE: Get tapes of songs popular in the 20's, 30's and 40's such as *Let Me Call You Sweetheart, Down by the Old Mill Stream, When You Wore a Tulip, Sleepy Time Gal.* Try your music stores or write *Recordings for Recovery* (See Reference for address.) They will provide any type of music on tape at no cost other than a blank tape. Gather residents together and play a little of each song and see who can guess the song title first. Give prizes if desired.

NEWSLETTER ASSISTING AND OTHER MAILINGS: If your facility puts your newsletter together in-house, gather residents who are able and let them stamp, staple, fold, sort and stuff envelopes. If desired, serve refreshments when finished.

NEWSPAPER FASHIONS: Give residents who are able a stack of newspaper, ribbons, paper clips, scotch tape, yarn and artificial flowers, and have them work in pairs. Let one person create a dress or shirt on their partner and then switch roles. Have other residents judge whose is the best. Give prizes if desired. This activity not only gives residents a chance to laugh but allows them to be creative. Rather than in pairs they can work on teams, which is more fun.

NURSERY RHYMES: Residents once learned nursery rhymes well, and many of them can still recite them. Get a book of rhymes at the library. Spend an hour with residents and give them the first line and let them recall the rest. This activity is usually very well received. It brings back many pleasant recollections.

PAPER DOLLS: Again, this may sound silly, but paper dolls were a standard toy long ago. Buy paper dolls anywhere, or go to your local museum. Sometimes they carry books to sell of "old-time" paper dolls that were popular long ago. Also, the *Gibson Girl*, a series of legendary pen and ink drawings showing a lovely girl in a series of different activities. (Paper dolls from long ago can also be purchased from *Dover Publications*. See Reference.)

PAPER POTLUCK: This sounds like a corny activity, but residents take it as seriously as if it were a real potluck. Cut from magazines pictures of food in several categories: meat, fish, soups, bread, vegetables, fruits, desserts and snacks. Arrange each food group on a separate tray. Give every resident a paper plate, and pass the trays so they can leisurely select the paper food. They can take as much as they want of any kind of food. It is surprising; residents most often take good food over the desserts. When residents have selected their food, you might have your dietician talk a little about a balanced diet. It's also a good chance for her to see what foods residents like, and it may provide new menu ideas.

PICTURE-TAKING DAY: Announce a week in advance that photographs will be taken on a given day. This gives residents something to look forward to and time to fuss, worrying about what they will wear. Arrange a nice background and schedule residents so you can have time for them all. You will probably have to begin early in the morning. Couples should get two photos taken, individually and as a couple. When the photographs are developed, fill a prominent bulletin board with all your residents' pictures. At the top of the board, put some meaningful words such as *Meet our Family!* This allows residents a chance to feel a part of a family within the facility and also to see what they really look like.

PIZZA PARTY: This is an easy activity and can well be held once a month since residents love it. Purchase inexpensive pizzas at the supermarket and heat them in the kitchen, unless your budget allows for you to order pizzas and have them delivered. Allow about two pieces per person. Serve this with punch or 7-Up. This activity gives residents a chance to try a food that wasn't popular in their day and also an opportunity to sit with residents they may not know and become acquainted. It provides fellowship, too, for those who already know each other.

POEM RECALL: Ask residents to recite a poem they once learned. You might give them the first line of a familiar one such as: "I think that I shall never see, a poem as lovely as a tree" or a line from *The Village Blacksmith*. You might give the first line of a nursery rhyme or ask about singing geography that they learned in school. Another way is to play some common poems on tape. If they cannot think of a poem, ask for the lyrics of a song they might remember. Give some hints such as "You'll look sweet upon the seat"... and no doubt someone will say "a bicycle built for two." This could be charted as reminiscence therapy.

POPCORN PARTY: Perhaps you have a no-show and don't know what to do. Put the popcorn popper on, and let residents enjoy visiting while munching on their popcorn. It doesn't require a no-show to make popcorn, though. It's a successful activity anytime—for residents and for staff. When the smell begins to permeate the facility, you'll have a lot of heads peeking in and asking for a sample. Make plenty!

PRICE IS RIGHT: Residents have generally been away from shopping for some time so today's prices are apt to baffle them. Before work, go through your cupboards and fill a couple bags with groceries. Try to find staple-type articles that the residents would have purchased when they did food shopping. Some suggestions: oatmeal, corn flakes, salt, spices, laundry soap, hand soap and tomato soup. Be sure to know the price you paid for each item. For the activity, hold up an item and tell residents what it is. Ask each resident to put in a guess. Write them all down. Announce who gets closest. This is a good current events-type activity to help orient them with present prices.

QUILTING: Collect scrap fabric. Cut a six-or eight-inch square from rough sandpaper. Lay this block on the wrong side of the fabric, and draw around it using a dark marker or chalk until many squares are drawn. Let residents cut out the squares. When finished, have those who like to sew assemble the blocks to the size of a full bed sheet (81" by 108" used to be standard, but I think they have cut that down a little).

Purchase quilt batting for the middle layer and a new sheet for the back. Lay the sheet on the floor, wrong side up. Top this with quilt batting the same width. On top of the batting, place the pieced block top, right side up. Use quilting pins, and pin the three thicknesses together all around the edges and at various places throughout the quilt. Use yarn and big-eyed yarn needles to draw small pieces of yarn through the three thicknesses at the center of each block. You might need needlenose pliers to pull the needle. Cut this yarn leaving about three inches. Have residents tie three knots in this yarn, and then trim to about 1 inch. Attach a border of fabric or ribbon that complements a predominant color in the quilt. This will take many activity sessions.

RADIO: Play tapes of old radio shows like *Jack Benny*. (See Reference for *Recordings for Recovery*.)

REMINISCENCE GROUP: Residents love to look back and discuss days of long ago. This makes a good weekly activity. Just introduce a subject of long ago, ask the right questions, and the residents will do the rest. Two books that have been especially designed and written for the A.D. to lead a lively group without any prior planning are: *Remembering the Good Old Days* and *Looking Back*. All the questions are there for you to ask. (See Reference.)

RHYTHM BAND: Everyone likes music of some sort. Form a band. Purchase rhythm band instruments, or make your own with odds and ends like pie pans, blocks covered with sandpaper that are rubbed together, bells, washboard and large salt and pepper shakers half-filled with beans or rice.

SHOE POLISHING DAY: Many residents haven't polished shoes in years. Have each resident bring a pair of shoes. Gather everyone around a table. Provide different colors of shoe polish and rags, and let them go to work. Get them talking about the shoe shine boy who used to work in barbershops.

SHOW AND TELL: On a given afternoon, invite everyone to come, but tell them they must bring something that is special to them. It may be a picture, jewelry, plant, an antique or an afghan. Have each resident tell a little about their contribution. Serve an interesting food treat. This activity helps those who don't talk much to open up and share and to make new acquaintances.

SING-A-LONG: These are always great when someone comes in, plays music and leads residents in singing.

SING-A-LONG 2: When you have a little time to fill, put on a tape residents know and encourage everyone to sing along.

SOAP BUBBLES: Invite in a group of children and assign one to each adult. Give each some soap bubbles. A large bottle can be divided into small medicine cups to save money, and wire can be bent for blowers. Put on the song *I'm Forever Blowing Bubbles* and let the children and the adults take turns blowing bubbles together. Serve refreshments when finished.

STAFF CRAFTS: Set the date, and enlist staff members to bring in crafts that they have done. It might be a knitted or crocheted afghan or ceramics or a painted picture. Collect as many as you can. Display them and assemble residents to spend an afternoon checking them out and talking about handiwork they used to do or still do.

STORY TELLING: Begin reading a traditional story with which residents are all familiar and know the real ending. An example might be *Snow White and the Seven Dwarfs* or *Pinocchio.* Ask the residents to make up a new ending for the old story. They can also make up an entire story. You might begin by setting a scene : "The barn door creaked opened, and I jumped back in fear." Let each resident add a little more to the story until it reaches a satisfying ending.

TAPE DAY: Most residents have probably never heard their voices on tape. Occasionally record activities where the residents are talking or playing. Then spend an afternoon playing with a tape recorder. Play back what's recorded and point out events and voices. Encourage residents to say something and let them listen to their voice. Some residents will be hams and want to talk and perform. Let them. This is a day for residents to laugh and have a good time.

TYPING: Bring in several typewriters and a computer if one is available. Encourage residents to try their hand at typing, especially those who once knew how to type. Let residents feel the difference between manual, electric and electronic typewriters as well as a computer. Have them all type their names.

WILD GAME HUNT: Buy two or three dart guns with rubber suction-type darts. Have residents cut pictures of wild animals from *National Geographic* or outdoor and sports magazines. Also look for large animal picture posters. Hang these on a long wall. Line residents up and let each have five shots to see how many animals they can hit. This provides a competitive spirit for residents and also brings back memories for men of hunting days.

WINTER PICNIC: If residents can't get outside for a picnic, bring the picnic to them. In the center of a room, arrange plastic flowers in a large container to simulate a flower garden. Arrange lawn chairs for residents to sit in. Serve a picnic lunch of fried chicken, potato salad, baked beans and cookies on styrofoam plates. After lunch play summer games like horseshoe or kick ball inside.

Chapter 3

Games

BADMINTON: (See Volleyball.)

BALL ON A SHEET: Locate a flat sheet. Gather residents' chairs around to form a square shape, slightly bigger than the sheet. Let each resident take hold of the sheet's edge and hold it up. Place a 10 or 12 inch rubber playground ball in the center, and let them roll it back and forth by raising and lowering the sheet. The object is to keep the ball in motion and not to let it fall off the sheet. They love this activity, but their arms can become tired in a short time. (A large round table cloth works great, too.)

BASKETBALL, NURSING HOME STYLE: Residents get so involved in this game, they don't even recognize it as exercise. It's a great activity to be played with residents in your facility or with other groups from the community. Here's how to play it:

Any number can play. Use a volleyball-size rubber playground ball and a large, weighted reinforced cardboard bucket (like industrial soap comes in) or a weighted basket of some sort.

The game is played with everyone sitting down. Arrange residents in chairs and wheelchairs to form a large circle. Make a real or imaginary line across the center of the circle. This line determines the two teams, one team on each side of the line. It does not matter if teams have an uneven number of players. On this line, in the center of the circle, set the bucket basket.

Scoot chairs so residents are all approximately the same distance from the basket—three to seven feet. If you have strong shooters, your circle might be more egg-shaped with the better shooters on the long ends.

Someone—an activity director or a volunteer—will need to stand in the center of the circle next to the basket to retrieve the ball after each throw and return it to the next resident to shoot.

It's very helpful to have a score keeper who's not the retriever. Use a blackboard to keep score.

The game begins as one team shoots for the basket. If he makes the basket, the ball goes to the other team to shoot. He receives one point. If he misses his shot, but the ball does not cross the imaginary center line, his team can shoot again, though the ball is passed to the player sitting next to the first shooter. If he misses, and the ball still doesn't cross the line, it goes to the next player on his team. If he shoots and misses, but it crosses the center line, the opposite team gets to shoot in the same manner. The first team to 21 points is the winner.

You might give your teams names. Sports shops will sometimes donate tee shirts to sponsor your team. Be sure to get big numbers on the front of the shirts since residents sit for the game and they wouldn't show on the back.

When residents learn how to play the game, invite another facility to yours and teach the game to them. You may take turns traveling back and forth to each other's facilities. One monthly game with another facility is good. Play with school kids. It doesn't matter what age. The game is fun playing with anyone from kindergarten through college. You might challenge your local college coach and basketball team to come to your facility and play with your residents. It's great publicity! And even confused residents can play this game and often very well.

BEACH BALL FUN: Purchase a large colorful beach ball. Scoot several large tables together and seat residents around them. Give the ball to a resident and ask him to roll it to another resident. Keep it going without falling off the table.

BEAN BAG TOSS: Bean bags are an old-fashioned toy, and residents enjoy throwing them around. There are different ways to play with them. Have residents shoot for a basket with them and give a point for each one put in. You can also put a line with masking tape on the floor across the room and have residents throw the bags and see who gets the closest to that line. Or you can have them throw the bags and measure whose goes the farthest.

BINGO: Everyone knows residents enjoy bingo. It's wise to buy cards with big numbers so those with impaired vision can take part. You will probably want to advertise monthly in your newsletter your need for bingo prizes. Be sure to let churches and groups who come to your facility know you are always needing bingo prizes. If you have a *Big Lots* or a similar outlet store near you, you can buy inexpensively little gifts, candy and gum for prizes. Fruit bingo is a nice change where residents win fruit rather than prizes. Some facilities simply give dimes for prizes. You may want to give coupons which residents can save up and redeem for prizes. Giving out prizes can be handled in many ways. One I like is to arrange prizes on a tray and let residents select the one they like as soon as they bingo.

BOWLING: Bowling can be fun for residents. You might want to use a plastic bowling set and invite a nursery school or kindergarten in to bowl with residents. The children can help set up the pins each time. You may want to have someone build a ramp where a real bowling ball sits on the top. The residents simply push the ball down the ramp and hope to knock down real pins below. Bowling alleys will sometimes give you old pins and balls. Or you might want to take residents out to a bowling alley. Some bowling alleys offer free bowling during off-hours.

BUTTON SPINNING: This is an old-time entertainment, but residents will still enjoy it. Stand a large button on its side and see if they can get it to spin. Coins can be spun in the same manner.

CARDS: Residents can still enjoy many card games—euchre, pinochle, bridge, hearts, rummy or even old maid. You may want to set up a regular card game one morning a week.

CHECKERS: Checkers are an old form of fun. Sometimes men enjoy this game a lot. If possible, leave a checkerboard set up where residents can get to it at their leisure. You may wish to have checker tournaments occasionally.

CHESS: Occasionally you'll come across residents who can still play chess. This game can pass a lot of leisure hours for those residents.

CHINESE CHECKERS: This is another old game some residents like to play.

CRIBBAGE: Read the directions and help residents as needed.

CROQUET: This is an old-fashioned game that can be played outside on the lawn. It can be used in conjunction with a picnic, a family party or a school class visit.

CROSSWORD PUZZLES: These puzzles can be worked individually or in small groups or the puzzle can be drawn on a large blackboard and worked together in a group. This is a good *before lunch* activity.

DARTS: For safety reasons, use darts with rubber suction tips or magnets. Dart guns are also fun for residents. Attach wild animal pictures to the wall, and let residents go on a wild game hunt with their dart guns. Or put up targets that they can shoot for points.

DOMINOES: Residents may have forgotten how to play. Read the directions and play the game with them. If residents cannot play the game, let them make up their own games with them. They can match the numbers of dots or just stack them up.

DRAWING IN THE DARK: Gather residents together, and give each of them a pencil or marker and a piece of paper. Tell them what you want them to draw. Then quickly turn off the lights and have them draw something before their eyes become accustomed to the dark.

ERECTOR SETS: Some men can benefit from working with Erector Sets because they are given the opportunity to use simple tools like a screwdriver and work with screws, washers and nuts. This can be good therapy for them.

HORSE RACING: This is a game that comes with a long felt cloth marked like a race track. Plastic horses come with the game and also a large sponge die which is rolled to determine which horse moves. (See Reference for supplier: *Medical and Activity Sales.*)

HORSESHOE: You can buy hard rubber horseshoes in the toy or sports department of stores. Have someone make you a free-standing stake by attaching a cut-off broomstick into a weighted board base. Seat residents in a circle with the stake in the center of the circle on the floor, and let them take turns trying to make a ringer. It's wise to place lap robes or a quilt on the floor under the stake to help absorb sound and to protect the floor.

I SEE SOMETHING YOU DON'T SEE: One person is "it". He looks around the room and locates an object but doesn't tell what it is. Then he says, "I see something you don't see and the color is...." Then everyone asks questions until the item is guessed.

JACKS: These can be purchased in the children's department. Let residents play with them on the tables. Throw the ball up and try to pick up one jack, and before the ball bounces twice, catch it. Do this with all ten jacks. Then throw the ball up, pick up two jacks at a time and catch the ball. When they're all picked up, try three at a time, etc. Let residents take turns.

KICKBALL: (See Exercise below.)

LINCOLN LOGS: Though we never want to reduce our residents to children, games like *Lincoln Logs* can provide hours of constructive entertainment. See which man can build the best log cabin.

MARBLES: To boys of yesteryear, marbles were a regular beloved activity. The men will probably appreciate this game more than ladies. Let them teach you some of the old games they used to play. Some residents will enjoy just looking at the various kinds of marbles.

MONOPOLY: Being a long game, it's unlikely this game will be too popular with residents though some may still enjoy playing for a while.

PARCHEESI: Play according to the box directions.

PUZZLES: If you can leave a card table up with a jigsaw puzzle in progress, you might be able to involve residents who take part in nothing else. When no one is paying any attention to them, they may locate pieces and put them in place.

Also, don't hesitate to use puzzles with fewer pieces. A good one for residents is the United States of America puzzle. Most of them drilled long and hard on states and capitals when they were in school, and many still remember them. In addition, it does not come across as a toy as some picture puzzles do.

RACES: Residents often like competition. Hold races. Have walking races and wheel chair races if residents are capable and you have the permission of your facility's administrative staff.

RING TOSS: You can buy these games in board form with plastic rings or the kind that sit on the floor. Tally up points and, if desired, give prizes.

SCRABBLE: If you have a volunteer who can supervise this game, some residents may really enjoy it. You might also try the junior form of Scrabble.

SHUFFLEBOARD: Perhaps you have a game room or outdoor patio where this game is painted on the floor. If not, you might try chalk or masking tape and make your own game.

TICK TACK TOE: This game works well if done on a blackboard so all can see it.

TINKERTOYS: This may seem like a children's activity, but with a large enough set many things can be created. This is great exercise for stiff fingers. They can be used for alert or confused residents.

TOSS ACROSS: *Toss Across* provides good exercise as residents throw small bean bags while trying to flip over a hinged X or O. The game used to be popular. Garage sales are a good place to look if you can't find new ones.

TOURNAMENTS AND CONTESTS: There are any number of contests you can devise providing rewards or ribbons for the winners. Some might be: checkers, euchre, bridge, basketball and spelling bees.

VOLLEYBALL: Many facilities play balloon volleyball by making two teams with a dividing net between them. If a net is not available, cheese cloth or nylon netting can be tied between two chairs. The game is played sitting down. The balloon can be hit with the hands or with fly swatters or rolled up newspaper. Some use coat hangers held by the hook and spread out to form a circle. This circle is covered with   nylon hose.   The hook should be covered with tape to prevent anyone from getting hurt.

WANDERING BALL: Play music while a ball is being passed around. The old song can be sung. "The wandering ball goes round and round. To pass it quickly you are bound. If you're the one to hold it last, why then for you, the game is past, and you are out!" The person holding the ball backs out of the circle. The circle continually gets smaller until just two people are left. They pass it back and forth to music until one is eliminated and you have a winner.

YATZE: Yatze is an easy game for residents that simply requires rolling dice. A volunteer will probably be needed to help keep track of residents' rolls and tally their score sheet.

Chapter 4

Exercise

BEAR HUNT: This exercise was brought home by the author's children when they were in scouting years ago (author unknown). It's a fun way to get residents to exercise. It goes something like this:

Let's go on a bear hunt. Everybody—march! march! march! (Hand over brow) "What's that I see? It's a river, a big, big river.

> Can't go around it!
> Can't go under it!
> Can't go over it!
> Guess we'll have to swim it. (Everybody swim.)

Whew! That was hard, but we made it. Continue to march! march! march!

"What's that I see there? (Hand over brow.) It's a wheat field, a big, big wheat field.

> Can't go around it!
> Can't go under it!
> Can't go over it!
> Guess we'll have to go through it. (Everybody rub hands together.)

Swish! **Swish!** Swish!

Whew! Made it. Continue to march! march! march!

(Hand over brow) What's that I see there? It's a tree, a big, big tree.

> Can't go around it!
> Can't go under it!
> Can't go over it!
> Guess we'll have to climb it! (Everyone pretend to climb it.
> Up one side and down the other.)

Whew! We made it. Continue to march! march! march!

(Hand over brow) What's that I see over there? It's a cave, a big, big cave!

> Can't go around it!
> Can't go under it!
> Can't go over it!
> Guess we'll have to go through it!" (Feel way around in it.)

It's dark in here!

> I feel something big!
> I feel something warm!
> I feel something furry!

It's a BEAR!

Run! run! run! Back through the cave. Feel your way through.
Run! run! run! Climb up the big tree. Climb down the other side.
Run! run! run! Go through the wheat field. Swish! swish! swish!
(rub hands together.)
Run! run! run! You come to the river.
Swim! swim! swim!

WE MADE IT!"

BICYCLING: This certainly is not for everyone, but some residents are still capable of riding a 3-wheel bike. Make sure they are never left alone and have close supervision. Secure family permission.

EASY EXERCISE: Start with your eyes, Look up, look down, look right, look left. Do this five times. Open eyes, close eyes, five times.

Put your head on your shoulders, first one side, then the other, five times.

Make faces. Smile real big. Open mouth wide. Yawn. Make an ugly face. Make a clown face. Blow a kiss. Make a mad face. Make a surprised face. Show your teeth real big.

Lift your arms above your head.Put them out to your sides. Make small circles, then larger ones. Put them out in front of you. Put them down. Repeat this several times.

Now we're going boating and fishing.

Walk to the boat. March! March! March! March! March! March! March!

Climb in the boat. Row the boat out into the deep water.

Dive in the water and begin to swim. Do breast stroke. Do the back stroke. Do the dog paddle. Swim back to the boat. Pull yourself in the boat.

Row back to shore. Climb out of the boat.

March back home. March! March! March! March!

ANOTHER EXERCISE: Breathe deeply a few times. Now begin with the face. If you were surprised, what kind of a face would you make?. Open mouth, raise eyebrows. Hold that pose. Repeat 3 times.

If you were angry, what kind of a face would you make? Grit your teeth, then draw your lips tight while clenching your fists.

If you were happy, what kind of a face would you make? Smile real big. Stretch those muscles. Hold. Repeat. 3 times.

If you were a fish, how would you move your mouth? Pucker big, then smile broadly without opening your mouth. Hold. Pucker again, smile, pucker. Hold.

If you were sad, what kind of a face would you make? Squint your eyes, draw up your mouth and jaw. Hold. Repeat 3 times.

If you were nervous, what kind of face would you make? Clench your teeth, clench your fists. Relax. Repeat 3 times.

Touch your head to your chest and raise it back up, then down, up, down, up, 3 times. Lean your head back and then up, back and up, 3 times. Now lean your head toward your right shoulder. Down, up, down up, 3 times. Lean your head to left shoulder. Bring it up, then down, up, down, up, 3 times.

Lift your arms straight out in front of you. Lift them up over your head. Up, down, up, down, 3 times. Spread them out to the sides. Lift them up, then down, up, down, 3 times. Put them out to the sides and rotate them in small forward circles. Make larger circles. Now, rotate them backwards in small circles. Make larger circles.

Put your hands on your hips. Bend from the waist forward. Straighten up. Bend again and stretch a little. Bend one more time, straighten up. Bend again and bounce. Now, bend to the right, and raise back up. Bend to the left, and raise back up. Bend to the right again, and then the left. 3 more times each side.

Let your hands dangle at your sides. Now swing them gently back and forth. Up, back, up, back, up, back, 3 more times.

Holding your hands out in front, your palms facing up, bring your fingertips to your shoulders and then back out in front of you. Repeat this 3 times. Put your fingertips on your shoulders again, and straighten your arms out to your sides, then back to your shoulders, then out to your sides, 3 times. Put your fingertips back to your shoulders, and then bend them out in front of you again, back to your shoulders, 3 times, then out to the sides, 3 times.

Sitting in a chair, lift your feet off the floor pointing toes toward the ceiling. Now stretch your toes out to the front and then pull them back, out front, pull them back, out front, pull them back, 3 times.

Put your feet back on the floor. Rest a minute. Breathe deeply. Now lift your legs up together, as high as comfortable, then down, up, down, up, down. 3 more times.

Now, lift your right ankle off the floor, and make small circles with it. Do the same with your left ankle. Now try the right ankle again. Then the left. One more time. Right. Left.

Now hold on to the side of the chair and pretend you are riding a bicycle. Lift up your legs and bend your knees in a pedaling fashion.
Pedal, pedal, pedal.

Now march in place. Up, down, up, down, up, down. Hike, hike, hike.

Now, pretend you are a rag doll, and hang loose as if there are no bones in your body. Shake all over.

Give yourselves a hand.

KICK BALL: Gather residents, all sitting, in a close circle with almost no room between wheelchairs or regular chairs. Simply put a twelve-inch rubber playground ball on the floor in the middle of the circle and let them kick it back and forth. This is great leg exercise and both alert and confused residents enjoy the activity.

RECORD: *Stay Fit While You Sit* is all that's needed for residents to have a real workout. Simply put this record on and lead the residents in doing the prescribed exercises. The only drawback, I've found is that too much time is devoted to breathing deeply and residents seem to tire of that. Just move the record forward at that point and skip that section if you wish.
(See Reference for address of record.)

SIMON SAYS: Everyone knows this traditional game where you give commands and no one obeys unless "Simon says" to do it. Example: Simon says, "Lift your right arm." Simon says, "Lift your left arm." "Put it down." No one is to put it down unless Simon tells him to do it. As you know, the object is to try to catch them exercising without Simon's permission. This is a fun way to involve your residents in exercise.

SINGING EXERCISE: Have residents sing along and make up movements to these: *Did You Ever See a Lassie? Mulberry Bush, Itsy Bitsy Spider, Row, Row, Row Your Boat, A Hunting We Will Go, Looby Lou.*

WALKING: You might wish to form a walking club and have those who wish to take part sign up. Chart their distance each time. It may only be to the end of the hall and back for some. If that is all they're capable of, that's fine. Help them work up to longer distances. In good weather you might be able to take residents outside for a walk. Give incentives. Perhaps visit some site on the way or stop for an ice cream or a cup of coffee. Give prizes or recognition for meeting goals.

YO-YO: Give residents a yo-yo and see if they can still work it. It's great exercise for the wrist.

Chapter 5

Monthly Biggies

BABY-LOVING DAY: This is an easy activity that brings great benefits. Rather than the traditional baby contest, just invite babies in for residents to love. Ask friends, residents' families and staff members to bring in their babies and pre-school children. In addition, advertise using public service announcements on radio, T.V., and newspaper. You probably won't get a lot of babies from the public sources, but it lets everyone know that your facility is busy doing fun activities. Send out notices a couple of weeks in advance of your Baby Loving Day. The first time or two, invite the press as well.

Arrange residents in the activity room sitting in chairs or wheel chairs to form a very large circle. When the mothers and babies arrive, let them get in the middle of the circle. Have a few toys there. Balls, balloons or bean bags are good for starters. The children, if old enough, will soon begin to play and will reach up to involve the residents in their play. The little ones can be held by the residents with their mothers available to supervise. When the visiting is about done, serve animal cookies and juice.

Baby Loving Days work well to hold about four times a year. After one or two, the mothers may well be calling you to see when you're having another one.

BABY CONTEST: Locate all the babies you can asking friends, residents' families and staff members to help you locate babies. Advertise using public service announcements. It is important that every baby wins something so no one goes home feeling bad. List as many categories as you can think of: cutest smile, most hair, friendliest, smartest, best personality, biggest and most petite. Then you may want to have an overall winner. Set up a registration table. As the mother signs up her child, have her place the child's name in one or more categories. Have three or five residents sit at a head table with name tags on reading "Judge."

After everyone is registered, have each mother bring her little one up and introduce him/her and tell a little about the child: age, only child, special likes, pets. Then she should present her child to the judges and sit down. Generally, the resident judges can pick their choices but will need some help keeping the

Monthly Biggies

Monthly Biggies

categories straight. Be prepared to help or have a volunteer do it. Don't be surprised, though, if the baby that residents choose is very fat and not the one you would choose. They sometimes have a different perception than we do of what makes a cute baby.

This is an activity that may bring you a good story in the paper or a feature on the evening local T.V. news.

BALLOON LAUNCH: Purchase large balloons and rent a helium tank. Blow up the balloons with helium, and tie a string with an attached card on the end of each balloon. On the card, stamp your facility's name, address and phone number and put a resident's name as well as the launch date on each card. Ask for a reply. Put this card in a small zip-lock bag to protect it from the elements. Let the residents launch their balloons and hopefully they will receive answers by those who find their cards. They will probably come from other states.

BALLOON RIDES: Locate someone who pilots a balloon and ask them to bring it to your facility. Have him offer tethered balloon rides to residents and visitors. If the community is invited, this can be a great public relations tool. Even if they are not, it's a great story for the press to pick up on. Be sure to invite families of residents who may want a short ride. Residents not riding will enjoy watching the balloon and others riding. This would be great entertainment at a resident/family picnic. Certainly not all your residents will want to try this one but you may find a few. Be sure to get written permission from their families before allowing residents to go up.

BRIDAL SHOW: Ask former brides and bridesmaids to model their dresses and wedding gowns. Again, to advertise, use public service announcements as well as asking staff, friends and residents' families to help you locate former brides. Perhaps some of the residents' family members still have their wedding gowns and would model them. Ask your museum to bring a gown and let someone model it. Get the wedding march on tape and play it as the brides model their gowns. Provide a simple wedding cake and punch for dessert. This is a good June activity.

BRIDAL SHOWER: Is a staff member getting married and are your residents curious about it? Why not let residents throw a shower for her? Invite other staff members, the bride's family, and residents' families whom you think might enjoy coming. Perhaps your administrator will allow you to hold it during the usual work day with staff members stopping for a few minutes as their schedule allows. If not, hold it in the evening. Share old-time bridal customs and wives' tales. (See *Word Games, superstition.*) Let residents each give the bride-to-be a piece of advice for a successful marriage. Let her open gifts in front of the residents. Perhaps the residents can give a single gift purchased through the activity fund or maybe they can make it. (A pieced patchwork comforter, tied and knotted with yarn, would be an example of a lovely gift. (See *Clubs, sewing.*)

CAMPING TRIP: Plan an overnight camping trip for residents. Check with local churches who have access to a lodge or clubhouse with sleeping accommodations. Take several volunteers and carry in the needed food. You might let residents try fishing, swimming and hiking (in moderation, of course). Have a wiener roast and a sing-a-long around a campfire. Take along checkers and a deck of cards for those who don't feel like more strenuous activities.

CELEBRITY DAY: Make a list of interesting community people to invite. It's fun for residents if you include many who have some sort of uniform to wear. These add color and make the event more impressive. These might include: policemen, firemen, Army, Navy, Marine or Air Force recruiters, minister or priest in collar, college or high school basketball stars in uniform, cheerleaders, scout leaders, boy and girl scouts and a doctor (with stethoscope, of course.) Go through your phone book and list interesting people such as state senators and representatives, the mayor, city clerk, a well-known disc jockey, local T.V. anchor man and the editor of your newspaper.

Involve your residents. Have them make name tags and help arrange simple refreshments—perhaps cookies and punch. Decorate with patriotic red, white and blue. Display the American flag. Have the activity last only one hour and guests can come in and out as their time allows. Be sure to call the press because this is a very worthwhile story that should net you publicity.

CHRISTMAS IN JULY: When the Christmas tree goes up in July and Christmas decorations appear in the activity room, there's going to be a lot of gossip about what's going on and if maybe the activity director is losing it. Just laugh. Plan a whole week of activities celebrating Christmas in July. Let residents help decorate the tree. Make Christmas cookies one day, candy another. Hold a Christmas sing-a-long one afternoon, and another have a minister hold an out-of-season Christmas service. On Friday offer a Christmas party and let residents unwrap little gifts (robbed from the bingo prizes). Serve popcorn balls or something similar and red punch. This activity should bring you a spot on the local T.V. evening news. Remember to send your press release out about two weeks before the actual event.

COTTON CANDY MAKING: Rent a cotton candy machine for an afternoon and whip up this old-fashioned treat for residents. It's kind of messy, but it will prove to be a fun afternoon. Maybe you can borrow a machine from someone who owns one and then solicit him to come and make the cotton candy.

DOG SHOW: This activity is a good one to be held during summer months when kids are free to bring their dogs, but it is certainly not limited to that time. Adults, too, love to show off their pets. Advertise with free public service announcements. Call your animal shelter and ask them to bring dogs in for the show. As in the baby contest, make categories so all dogs win something. You might include the: smartest dog, sleepiest, biggest, smallest, friendliest, best behaved, longest hair, and most unique.

For prizes purchase small plastic trophies from a supply house, or give ribbons. These can be made from funeral bouquet ribbons. Simply cut out an animal from construction paper and staple a wide piece of ribbon to it—blue for first place, red for second and white for third. You might let them glue on some gold stars for glitter.

EASTER EGG HUNT: (See *Community*.)

FASHION SHOW: There are many ways to hold fashion shows. Residents can be the models and model their own best outfits. Or you can invite a store in to hold a fashion show for residents. A theatre group or a museum may put on a fashion show for you using period clothing. If held the day before Easter, you can invite young children in to model their new Easter fashions.

Provide a stage and decorate it with flowers or plants. Write a script introducing each model and describing each outfit. If using your residents as models, be sure to include some men. This can also be a funny fashion show where you provide silly outfits for residents to model and give everyone a good laugh.

HOBO DAY: Include staff by asking everyone to find their best old beat-up hat, man's suit coat and oversize trousers. They may want to visit the Goodwill store. Work with the kitchen and prepare a sack lunch tied up in a paper bag and attached to a dowel rod. Supply tin pie plates to use when residents open their sacks. Hobo Stew (vegetable soup or beans) may be served also. Have residents tell stories in the afternoon about hobos who came to their door. Perhaps they even hopped a train or two during tough times. Let them tell you about those days. Invite a fiddler in to play.

ICE CREAM SOCIAL: This can be done in two ways. You can have them make homemade ice cream in freezers and serve it, or you can purchase gallons of ice cream, chocolate syrup, strawberry preserves (thinned with water) crushed pineapple, bananas and whipped cream. Solicit some resident help in taking orders and constructing the sundaes.

KITE FLYING: In spring or in good kite flying weather, invite a class of school children (about 7th grade), or cub scouts or boy scouts to your facility to fly kites with residents. They can bring kites and you can provide several more. Take residents outside or to an open area where they can watch and perhaps hold the strings as the kites fly high. Provide popcorn or cookies and canned soda for the children. You might want to hold a contest to see whose flies the highest and give a prize.

MOTEL GET-A-WAY: If your budget allows or families will pay, take a few of your residents who do not need a lot of medical care on a short vacation. Locate a motel within 50 or 60 miles from your facility so they have some travel time. Stop along the way for a picnic lunch. Try to take a nurse along for emergencies and for passing meds. For convenience, you will probably want residents to take their meals at the hotel dining room. You might sightsee one afternoon or take in a movie though the motel stay in itself will probably be enough stimulation for a real vacation.

OLYMPICS: Here's a chance to join with other facilities and to let your residents meet new people their own age and to have a great time. Call other nursing homes or facilities and find those interested. (They probably all will be). Next locate a free place to hold an olympics such as a school gym or community center. Ask each facility to give a donation—about $25.00—to cover expenses: ribbons, trophies, helium balloons and refreshments. As your space permits, determine how many residents each facility may bring. A hundred residents makes a workable olympics. Get two or three A.D's involved helping you put on the olympics.

Plan simple competitive activities. Here's some that have worked well elsewhere: wheelchair races, wheelchair obstacle courses, walking races, free-throw contests, bucket basketball, bean bag toss, flying saucers (paper plates sailed through suspended hula hoops), bean bags in a clown mouth and horseshoe. As the grand finale, have a dance contest with dancers from Arthur Murray Dance Studios judging. Give ribbons and small plastic trophies to winners. Present participation ribbons so no one goes home without something.

Begin the event with a parade. Have a few residents from each facility march around the gym behind a banner they have made bearing their facility's name. March to the tune of *When the Saints Come Marching In*. Solicit an emcee such as a disc jockey. You might want to have a band, kitchen-type or otherwise, play between events. Serve simple refreshments such as popcorn and orange drink. This is best left till the event is nearly over. Give everyone a helium balloon. You can tie them to the wheel chairs for color during the event. This is a big event and can bring good publicity as well as much fun and a sense of competition for residents.

PAJAMA PARTY: About the facility, put up posters announcing the pajama party. Alert staff members so they can help remind residents. Have them come in their night clothes—pajamas and robes and with curlers if they like. Light the fire if you have a fireplace, if not, create a make-shift campfire using a red light bulb in an extension cord or small lamp. Show a comedy movie. Make popcorn and hot chocolate. Reminisce about parties long ago.

PET SHOW: (See *Dog Show* above.)

QUEEN CONTEST: Nominate a few female residents who will be able to take part. Have gentleman, if possible, escort each potential queen up to the front of the room. Use a trellis for decoration and for the contestants to walk or wheel under when being introduced. Have a series of questions prepared to ask the contestants. From their answers, let residents judge which one they want. Have a 3rd, 2nd, and 1st runner up. Lastly, announce the queen, and let her walk or wheel under the trellis. Present her with a bouquet of flowers and a gift. Take her picture.

QUILT SHOW: Contact a quilting club in your area, and ask if they'd be willing to show several quilts at a resident quilt show. Also you might ask individuals you know who do quilting to bring theirs to show. Beforehand decide where you will display the quilts. You can drape them over heavy furniture such as pianos or hang them on portable clothes racks. Quilting members generally have quilt stands so be sure to ask when you book them up. Allow residents to inspect the quilts, and if you like, make it a contest with residents judging which quilt they like best. Award small trophies or a homemade ribbon or a simple gift to winners.

SCHOOL DAYS: In late August or early September, let residents relive a day of school. Begin the school day with the *Pledge Allegiance to the Flag.* In the morning, review states and capitals. Give them the capitals and let them give you the states. Review mathematics tables with residents. Have the kitchen provide sack lunches. Over lunch break, do some marching in place, and play some basketball at recess. In the afternoon have a spelling bee and then a reminiscent session where residents can share what they remember about their actual school days.

SENIOR PROM: Locate a band that plays music of the 30's and 40's. Invite family members if you like. You might want to ask a college fraternity and a sorority if they'd come to your prom and help dance with residents, especially those in wheelchairs. Have the staff dress the residents in their Sunday best. Be sure to have them add a little perfume and jewelry. Provide an inexpensive corsage (artificial flowers) for each lady resident and a boutonniere for each man. Locate a trellis at the entrance to the dance. Sometime during the evening, take each resident's picture with a "date." Cover small tables with cloths and provide a nice candle in the center. Turn the lights down low. When the music begins, encourage someone to start the dancing. Serve simple refreshments in as fancy a manner as possible. The prom need last only an hour and a half. It can be a romantic evening for residents and like a date of long ago.

TALENT SHOW, RESIDENT/STAFF: Make up a stage or borrow one. Locate a P.A. system. Decorate your facility luxuriously. Staff members may perform alone, with other staff members or with residents. You might have guitar players, gospel singers, piano players, a comedy act, a clown act, a Minnie Pearl or Charlie McCarthy act. Intermingle staff performances with resident performances. Invite families or the general public.

TALENT SHOW, KIDS: This is a good activity to hold in the summertime when kids are out of school. Short of that, choose a Saturday. Use public service announcements and personally invite children. You might have a baton twirler, tap dancer, gymnast, singer, pianist or an artist. Give little plastic trophies for first, second and third places. Provide participation ribbons so no one goes home disappointed. You may want to serve simple refreshments.

WEDDING, MOCK: This can be a hilariously funny activity if you have a few residents with a great sense of humor. Even if you don't, you'll find residents looking forward to it as if it were a real wedding. Locate residents to be the bride and groom, best man, matron of honor, father of the bride, mother of the bride and judge or preacher. Arrange some sort of costumes: a fur for the mother of the bride, a shotgun (toy) for the father of the bride and big hats for the brides maid. The bride can wear a white nightgown and a bedsheet drawn up at one end with wire wrapped around that end and flowers attached to the wire. Find a wild suit jacket for the groom.

The idea is to make this as funny as possible. Unwind a roll of red and white checked plastic table covering on the floor for the bride to walk down the aisle on. Have a funny wedding cake—just something you bought at the grocery with a silly topping such as Snoopy or something equally inappropriate for a wedding. Write a silly ceremony.

Record the wedding march and play it when your wedding starts. Have the bride walk, wheel or be pushed in a wheel chair down the aisle. During the ceremony, have the father keep the play shotgun pointed at the groom. When it's over, celebrate with a reception. Residents love this activity and they take their parts very seriously.

Here's a sample silly ceremony written for two particular residents who possessed colorful personalities and great senses of humor.

We are joined here together in the presence of these witnesses to join this couple in *hokey macaroni*. This good old-fashioned, make-believe *weeding* will join Lily Feisty Jones and Sammie Tiger Hathaway.

Sammie, will you take this gentle-natured woman to be your make-believe madam to have and to hold till 3:00 do you part?

SAMMIE: I'll consider it.

Lilly, will you take this rattlesnake loverboy to be your unlawfully loaded doom till 3:00 you do part?

LILLY: "I might as well.

With this ring, we'll probably turn red....

By the authority vested in me as comedian of this XYZ facility, I now pronounce you man and strife!

You may kiss your bride."

(And the bride added "May this macaroni ceremony produce many little spaghetti(s).)

WESTERN DAY: Locate as many cowboy hats as you can borrow, and let the men take turns wearing them. If your budget allows, buy men's red handker-chiefs as neck scarves for the men. Secure them with a plastic curtain ring. Locate a few bales of hay or straw and put in the activity room. Find a couple saddles and place these over wooden sawhorses. Take a six-foot long 2' by 4' and pound big nails in it. From these nails, hang bridles and other horse accessories. You might rest this board on the fireplace mantle or lay it on the edge of a high piece of furniture. Serve a lunch of beans and cornbread or roast beef sandwiches. Ask residents to reminisce about earlier days and cowboys. Ask if any of them were cowboys. Ask who the cowboy movie stars were long ago. (No doubt Tom Mix will be at the top of the list.) Throughout the day play records or tapes of Gene Autry and Roy Rogers. Contact square dancers as the main entertainment. Between their dancing let them sit on the bales of hay or straw. You may want to invite the families of residents to share in the entertainment.

Crafts

Crafts

Chapter 6

Crafts

BIRD FEEDER: Collect a few plastic lids that come on coffee or shortening cans. Buy a jar of inexpensive peanut butter and a bag of all-purpose bird seed. Poke a hole near the edge of the plastic lid and run a sturdy ribbon or string through it about 12-inches long. This will be the hanger. Have residents spread peanut butter in the lid and then sprinkle that with bird seed. Have them lightly push the seed into the peanut butter until it stays firm. Hang these from a tree or something stationary near a window where residents can watch the birds enjoy their creations.

BOTTLE SNOWMAN: You will need a bleach bottle (gallon or 1/2 gallon for each resident and sand or small rocks to weight them. Also gather black ribbon, black buttons, 5" styrofoam balls, small twigs, and large-headed straight pins. The bottle handle will be the back. Have residents make a hole in the styrofoam ball and then push it over the mouth of the bleach bottle for the head. Let them place a piece of ribbon around the middle of the bottle for a belt and secure it with a pin in back. They can push pins through the buttons into the styrofoam ball for eyes.

Poke holes for them (a heated ice pick works well) in each side of the bottle and let them push in the twigs for arms. Give each resident a sock to roll down and place on the head for a hat. Give them each a scrap of fabric and let them fashion a scarf and secure it with a pin.

BOTTLED BEANS: These make attractive decorations but can be given as lovely gifts. You'll need several varieties of beans, lentils, rice, and quart jars with canning lids. Let residents make one-inch layers of each, contrasting color and texture. Fill the jar in this way. Using pinking shears, cut 5-1/2 inch circles from gingham or other colorful cotton fabric. Let residents drape this over the mouth of the jar and screw on a canning jar ring.

BOTTLED PASTA: Following the directions for bottled beans, substitute various shapes and colors of pasta: noodles, spinach noodles, macaroni and shells.

BOTTLE DOLL, SEWING: Collect Mrs. Butterworth syrup bottles that are formed in the shape of a large woman. From this make a glass doll whose apron holds spools of thread and needles. Purchase several small rolls of thread in assorted colors. Let residents paint the molded dress on the bottle or just the collar and cuffs if they wish with enamel or acrylic paint. Paint the bottle top to match the dress. Let dry. Help them cut a scrap of fabric into a 4-inch circle. This will be placed over the spout of the bottle for a brim and then the painted top will be screwed on over this to complete the doll's maid cap.

From another scrap of fabric approximately 8 inches wide and 9 inches long, fashion an apron that will tie around the bottle's waist. Have residents sew a narrow hem in one end though which a ribbon or string will be run to form a gathered belt. Run a small hem on the wrong side of the apron on the bottom end. Now fold up the bottom of the apron until it just touches the bottom of the bottle. Press up. Every one and a half inches, tack this fold up until you are across the apron. This will form small pockets. In each pocket, insert a small spool of thread. Place a needle and a few pins in the apron front.

BOXES, MACARONI: Select the size box you wish. Cigar boxes are nice, if available. Otherwise, any small box will do. Buy dry macaroni (in a variety of shapes if desired) and let residents glue it all over top and sides of the box. When the glue is dry, spray the macaroni-covered box with gold paint.

BREAD DOUGH ORNAMENTS: (See *Crafts, Christmas.*) Roll dough and shape into flowers, animals, fruit or desired shape, or use cookie cutters. Paint with acrylic paint. Decorate animals with tiny eyes, pipe cleaners and trim.

BUTTERFLIES: Fold a 3 by 6-inch piece of tissue paper, cellophane or aluminum foil so that it is pushed together in the middle to resemble a butterfly. Fasten a 2-inch long pipe cleaner in the center with wire. Leave the two ends of the wire for the antenna. Stick a long pin through the center of the butterfly and into the eraser of a new pencil. This makes a whirl-a-gig that will blow around in the wind or when you blow on it.

CANDLES, SAND: Fill a small box (shoe box, milk carton or smaller) with sand. Add enough water to dampen sand. Scoop out a hole or screw your fist in the sand. Push your thumb and two fingers down in the sand. This will create leg molds for your candle so that it will stand up on three legs. Melt paraffin in a double boiler and add broken bits of crayon for color. Pour this melted wax in sand mold. While the wax is still hot, make a hole in the center with a toothpick or a wooden match. Put the wick in this hole and add a little more hot wax to seal the wick hole. When the wax is cool, remove your candle from the sand.

CANDLES, NUGGET: Collect all the old candles you can. You may well have quite a few lying in your activity cupboard. In addition to these, you will need slab candle wax. This is low temperature wax usually sold in 11 pound blocks (one block will make 16-1/2 pint candles or 4-1 quart candles). Also collect empty milk cartons—either quart ones or 1/2 pint milk cartons like those purchased for school children. Wash thoroughly. These will be your candle molds. You'll also need a double boiler or melting pot and a pan of water. An old pitcher or coffee pot works well. You'll want to have a wooden spoon to stir your wax and a cookie sheet lined with newspaper, or aluminum pie pans for each resident's candle when you actually pour the wax.

Have residents cut or break some of the old candle bits into small nuggets in various sizes and shapes. Reserve some for later. Set aside. Next, break the slab candle wax into pieces to fit into your double boiler or melting pot that has been set in a pan of water. A word of caution here! Never, even for a second, leave hot wax unattended.

Next, you will need a ready-made candle for each candle you plan to make. This need not be a whole new candle. It just needs to be as tall as you wish your finished candle to be. (If you do not have enough candles for this step, simply skip it). A candle wick can be purchased and added when your candle is finished). Insert this candle in the center of the milk carton and secure it by pouring in the base around it a 1/2-inch layer of hot wax. Let this harden. (This is done so you will not have to put a wick in later.)

Have residents drop some broken candle pieces into the bottom of the milk carton mold to about 1/3 full. Pour melted slab wax over this to 1/2 inch of crushed candle pieces. Have residents add another 1/3 carton of candle bits. Again pour the hot wax over this. Repeat until the milk carton mold is full or as tall as you wish your candle to be. End with melted wax. If your candle develops a well in the center, pour in some more melted wax. Pour any left-over wax into an empty milk carton to be used at another time. Let the candles cool at room temperature.

If you've skipped the step of putting a used candle in the middle of each mold, now use an ice pick or sharp object and poke a hole through the whole candle. Insert the wick. Pour more hot melted wax in the hole around the wick and let it harden.

Note: Slab wax, when melted, should remain at 145 degrees. Do not leave hot wax unattended or let residents handle it. This part should only be done by an activity director or volunteer.

CHUNK CANDLES: Fill about 1/3 full, a quart or half-gallon paper milk carton with ice pieces (not finely crushed). Melt paraffin in the top of a double boiler, and add some broken crayons pieces for color. Pour this over the ice pieces. Add 1/3 more ice and again pour paraffin over this. This may be a separate mixture of paraffin with different color crayons added if a multi-colored candle is desired. Add ice again and fill to near the top of the milk carton mold. Pour paraffin over this. When ice is melted but paraffin still soft, poke a hole down through the middle of the candle with an ice pick. Put in wick or a piece of heavy string. Pour more melted paraffin in the hole around the string to seal. When totally cool, remove the milk container and you have a chunk candle.

CANDY HOLDERS: Have residents cut 4-inch circles from colorful cotton fabric with pinking shears. Have ready some warm paraffin or a solution of heavy starch. Let residents dip their fabric circles in this, and then drape them over the bottom of jelly glasses or muffin tins. Secure each with a rubber band until dry. Fill with candy for party favors.

CANDY TRAIN: Give each resident a paper plate or square of cardboard as a base. Have them line marshmallows up to form a train. Glue these together with royal frosting (egg whites and powdered sugar beat together 7 minutes) or toothpicks. Push sturdy toothpicks through the marshmallows for axles and add Lifesavers for wheels secured with a raisin on the end. Create a happy face on the engine with round candies like M&M's. Decorate the rest of the train with colorful candies. Black licorice makes a nice track. Great gift for young children. (Be sure to warn them of the toothpicks).

CLOWN HATS: Great for parties or kids' visits. Use poster board or construction paper, and cut these in triangles that are rounded across the bottom rather than cut in a straight line. The edges should be about 12 inches long and the bottom point around 15 inches. Roll the paper into a cone and staple it. Let residents decorate it with markers or stickers. They can cut a round brim if they like and staple it on. Tassels can be fashioned from tissue paper stapled on the top for fringe.

DECOUPAGE KEY RINGS: Purchase tiny unfinished wooden key rings at a craft store. Have residents glue small decals, photographs or tiny pictures cut from magazines on them. Let them paint decoupage finish such as Mod Podge on both sides. Hang them up to dry. Put two or three coats of finish on them.

DOLL CRADLES: Collect several tomato baskets. These are long and narrow wooden baskets with a wire or wooden handle on top. (Check with roadside vegetable stands or supermarkets). Buy pink checked gingham fabric and wide white lace. Lay the basket on the side and form a newspaper pattern by wrapping around four sides. Trace around the bottom of the basket but cut this pattern about two inches larger all around. Cut two pieces of each of these patterns -- one for the outside and one for the inside. First, with *Modpodge*, or some other instant decoupage glue, affix the bottom fabric to the basket and bring up slightly around the sides. Next, glue the long strip of fabric around all the sides, both inside and out. When the box is completely covered, brush with a coat of instant decoupage. Glue wide eyelet lace around the edges to cover any rough edges. Cover the handle with ribbon or lace. Attach ribbons where desired. Add a baby doll or sock doll.

DOLLS: (See *Projects.*)

DRUM: This is a nice toy to give to youngsters, or residents may want to use them in their rhythm band. You will need cans: 2 or 3 pound coffee cans, shortening cans or 46-ounce juice cans, and scrap rubber from inner tubes. With the can opener, cut out both top and bottom of the cans. Paint the cans with enamel. Let them dry thoroughly.

Cut a circle out of newspaper for a pattern. This should be 1-3/4 inches bigger around than the can bottom. Cut your old inner tube open. Wash it off and turn inside out on a flat surface. Lay your pattern on the rubber tube, and trace with chalk. Cut it out with scissors. Make two for each drum. Punch holes with a punch about every two inches around the rubber.

Place one piece of rubber over the can top and one over the can bottom. Use twine or heavy plastic string, and lace the top and bottom pieces together, up and down over the drum frame,until you are around the drum. Pull the ends tightly in place and tie with a hard knot.

DYE, PAPER TOWELS: Fill muffin tins with a few drops of water and vegetable food coloring. Let residents fold paper towels in any way they wish. Dip these in the different colors in the muffin tins. Let them unfold and see their design.

FAN MAKING: Visit a wallpaper store and ask for wallpaper sample books that are no longer used. Use these for residents to make fans. Let them each choose a pattern they want for their fan. Cut it from the book and have residents fold it in half, then fold it accordion style. Let them tape the bottom end for a handle. Add flowers, lace and ribbon, and these can be hung on residents' doors.

FINGER PAINT: Provide residents with several bowls of fingerpaint and sheets of white paper. Let their imaginations run wild. Here's a fingerpaint recipe:

>   1 c. warm water
>   1/4 c. flour

Whip it up and add food color.

JACK IN THE MATCH BOX: Cut two strips of paper 10-inches long and 1/2-inch wide. Glue the end of one strip over the end of the other strip at right angles. (It will look like an "L".) Starting at this glued corner, fold one strip over the other, back and forth, at right angles, continuing until the end of the strip. This will look and act like a spring, popping up when it is released. Have residents draw a tiny funny face on construction paper to attach to the end of this paper spring. Glue to one end on the spring. Glue the other end of the string inside a small (not large kitchen matches) match box. Push the paper spring down and close the match box. When the box is opened, Jack will jump up.

JAR CRAFT: Baby food jars are wonderful craft starters. Residents can stick a small flower or leaf decal on each tiny jar and then paint the lids in a bright enamel paint. When thoroughly dry, the jars may be filled with assorted spices and baking supplies to delight any cook. They could be filled with buttons, pins and other sewing notions for the seamstress. If they are to be gifts for office workers, the jars might contain paper clips, rubber bands and push pins. Potpourri made from donated funeral flowers could also fill the tiny jars. For men a more masculine decal might be placed on the jars and they could be filled with small nails, screws, nuts, bolts and washers.

LEAVES IRONED: Let residents gather pretty green leaves. On a folded towel, have them pound their leaf with a small brush, or rub it gently for about five minutes until the center green part of leaf is lacy and veins are exposed. To preserve it, iron it between sheets of waxed paper.

MOBILES: Mobiles are wonderful items to hang in the rooms of bedfast patients. They can be made from many items. A clothes hanger makes an easy base. From it hang several strings, colorful yarn or fine wire. If desired, you may use a dowel rod wired crosswise across the hanger bottom, and from it hang even more strings. The strings can hold a variety of things—flower or animal pictures cut from greeting cards; miniature cut-outs of sun, moon and stars; or toilet paper and paper towel rolls cut and painted to look like miniature people.

NECKLACE: Let residents make a chain of paper clips by slipping one inside of the other to hook together. Once a good size chain is made, let them wrap different colors of plastic tape around the center of each clip. This forms a necklace, or if everyone's chains are attached, they can be hung on the Christmas tree.

NOODLE JEWELRY: Purchase various shapes of pasta, and let residents string it and make jewelry.

NUT DOLLS: Nut dolls were often made at Christmas long ago and children loved them. Collect a variety of nuts in different sizes (A bag of mixed nuts in the shell works well). Purchase string-type elastic. Some nuts can be pricked with a large needle near the end of the nut from one side through to the other. Elastic string can be run through this. If you can't prick the nut, use a hot glue gun to attach the elastic. Use a walnut for the head. Attach elastic, add a long shaped nut for the body. Add elastic for two legs and arms. Use hazelnuts or other small nuts for hands and feet. Paint eyes, nose, and mouth. (These can also be made using pine cones and acorns.)

PAPER DOLLS STRING: Give residents folded paper and let them cut out a string of paper dolls the way they did as children.

PIN CUSHION: Collect large empty thread spools. Let residents paint them. Cut 3-inch diameter circles from fabric and from felt. Put the right sides of the circles of felt and the circles of fabric together and let residents sew around them. Cut a hole slightly smaller than top of spool in center of felt; turn right side out; stuff with cotton. Dab glue around underside of spool rim; insert rim into hole in felt, stretching felt to fit the spool. Tack rickrack around pincushion.

PRINTING POTATOES: Either pre-cut, or if residents are able, let them cut potatoes in various shapes to be used for printing. Use stamp pads, tempera in dishes or water-soluble linoleum ink. Let residents stamp their potato cuts on unprinted newspaper or other plain paper to create wrapping paper.

SOAP ROPE: Save bits and pieces of soap or buy cheap bar soap and let residents crack it up with a hammer on a cutting board. Fill a double boiler with water 2/3 full. Let the top part of the pan heat up over the water. When it boils, reduce heat to low and add soap pieces. Keep stirring with wooden spoon until melted, and then pour into molds. Six-ounce juice cans work well. When the soap begins to cool and set, fold a   14-inch piece of thin rope in half and insert both ends into the can. Cool thoroughly and remove by dipping the can in warm water. These can be hung in residents' closets for a fresh smell, used for bathing or given as gifts.

STENCILING: Collect nice solid boxes like cigar boxes or shoe boxes. Paint the boxes. Spray paint works well. Purchase or make stencils. Let residents stencil on the boxes with fast-drying acrylic paint.

STRAW CONSTRUCTION: Join soda straws with paper clips. The clips may need to be pulled apart slightly to hold the straws together. Straws may be cut to make shorter pieces. Residents can fashion buildings, animals or people.

SWEET-SMELLING BALL: These may be hung in residents' rooms to give off a sweet aroma. Purchase oranges, lemons, limes or apples. You'll also need toothpicks, whole cloves, cheesecloth or nylon netting and powdered cinnamon.

You probably already have ribbon on hand. You will want to select good fresh fruit that is firm and not bruised. With a toothpick, let residents punch holes all over the fruit and fill these holes with whole cloves until the fruit is completely covered. Cut squares of cheesecloth or nylon net large enough to wrap each piece of fruit. Place the studded fruit on the cloth and sprinkle generously with powdered cinnamon. Tie a string and then a bow around the end of the cheesecloth and hang the fruit up somewhere to dry. The fruit will soon dry and shrink and become lighter. The sweet smell will grow yet sweeter. At this point it is ready to hang in a room or give as a gift.

TIE DYEING: Have laundry save old bed sheets for you or, if available, use cotton tee shirts. Give each resident a piece of cloth about a yard square or a cotton tee shirt. Use packaged dyes dissolved according to directions. Use less water for stronger colors. Help residents twist or neatly fold in small folds their piece to be dyed. Now secure it with rubber bands in various places. Carefully dip this in dye for a few seconds. When the rubber bands are removed they will have a unique pattern.

TREE, ALL-PURPOSE: Locate a forked branch off a tree. It should be approximately three to four feet tall when stood upright with several small twigs or limbs coming off it. Spray paint it white, gold or silver. Make a mixture of plaster of Paris and fill a large flower pot with it. When it is pretty well hardened, place your tree in it, and let it thoroughly set until the plaster of Paris is very hard.

Use your tree throughout the year. In the spring, you might want to wire artificial flowers on it. Residents could even make them from tissues or tissue paper. On Valentine's Day attach tiny valentines. During Thanksgiving week let residents and guests who visit your facility write on scraps of paper one thing for which they are thankful. Have them clip or tape these to the tree. Near Thanksgiving read them all. In fall add acorns and pine cones. At Christmas add bells, birds, or angels. There's no end to the decoration with which you can dress up your tree.

Christmas Crafts

BOOK MARKS: Let residents cut small felt triangles (approximately 1-1/2 inches) for the Christmas tree. Next, let them glue tiny lace or colorful felt pieces to the triangle and then sequins or buttons. Cut an inch-wide strip of felt several inches long and glue this to the bottom of the felt triangle.

BREAD DOUGH ORNAMENTS: Here's a large recipe.

> 8 c. flour
> 4 c. salt
> 3 - 3 1/2 c. cold water

Adding water in small amounts, mix the ingredients thoroughly with your fingers until all the dough sticks together. Then knead the dough for 10 minutes until smooth and elastic. Roll half the dough with a rolling pin into 1/4-inch thickness and place it on wax paper. Use Christmas cookie cutters, or make your own design and shape your ornaments. Use an ice pick or a sharp instrument to poke a hole in the top for the hanger. Place your ornaments on a greased cookie sheet and bake in a preheated 350 degree oven for one hour. Remove and cool. Use bright acrylic paints to paint the ornaments. After they have dried, place three coats of clear spray on them to protect them from cracking and breaking. Put a string through the hole and hang on the Christmas tree.

CHRISTMAS CARD PLACEMATS: Save old Christmas cards. Give residents a piece of poster board or construction paper the size of a place mat. Let them completely cover it on both sides with Christmas cards. They will overlap each other somewhat. Have them glue the cards down so they will stay. Help them cover both sides with clear contact paper. Let them use their mats at mealtime during the holiday season.

CHRISTMAS CARDS: Save old Christmas cards. Let residents cut out attractive pictures from these. Fold construction paper in card size shapes, and let residents glue the Christmas card picture cut-outs on these. Let residents, then, decorate as they wish with stars, glitter and sequins.

CHRISTMAS CROCHET DECORATION: When a lid is removed from a new plastic gallon jug of milk, a tiny plastic ring pulls off to be discarded. Save these rings. Let residents who can, crochet around them. Hang them on the Christmas tree to resemble snowflakes, or put them together to make a lovely Christmas mobile.

PAPER CHAINS: Like residents did when they were children, let them make paper chains from strips of red and green construction paper. Let them alternate the colors and paste or staple each loop to the one before. Each resident can make a chain and then they can attach them. The chains are attractive strung along the ceiling in the hallways or placed on the Christmas tree. They are especially nice if an old-fashioned decorating theme is used. Paper chains look lovely along with strung popcorn, pine cones, nut dolls and homemade ornaments.

PAPERWEIGHT, CHRISTMAS SCENE: You'll need a box of tapioca, clean small baby food jars, plaster of Paris, trinket decorations (check your Christmas decorations for broken ones), nylon net, and a strainer. Mix up a little plaster of Paris according to directions and give each resident a small ball (about 1" round) and let them put it inside the baby food jar lid. This may require a little glue. (There should be enough room left to screw the lid back on later). Before it hardens, let them push a tiny ornament or even miniature twigs into this.

Next day, have them fill the jars with water. The tapioca will create the snow. Let residents sift it through a fine strainer so your water won't end up cloudy. Sift it again. Add 1/4 teaspoon of this sifted tapioca to make the snow. To dress it up, cut two circles from your nylon net, one 5 inches and one 6 inches. Cut a three-inch circle from the green felt. Attach the lid to the jar. Lay the felt and then the net circles over the lid and secure with a rubber band. Turn it over and you have a paperweight.

PILL BOTTLE ORNAMENT: On green felt, trace around the top and bottom of the pill bottle. Cut out these felt circles and glue them to the top of the lid and bottom of the pill bottle. Remove the lid. Glue a piece of cotton to the inside of the lid to resemble a cloud. Glue a miniature figurine (these can often be retrieved from broken Christmas ornaments and decorations) on top of this cotton cloud and pull the cotton up behind a little. Glue narrow velvet ribbon around the (now) top of bottle and the edge of lid (now the bottom). Make a bow leaving three-inch streamers, and attach to the center of the felt on the lid. Glue a pretty button to the felt on the top. Let it dry. Using a glue gun, attach a colorful loop of string or braid at the center of the button for hanging.

SNOW MAN: Give residents each a piece of construction paper—red, green or black. Set out a bag of cotton balls and let them design snowmen on their paper. They may use just three balls for a tiny snowman or combine several to make a large one. Give them felt scraps, sequins, buttons and yarn to finish their creations. They may get very creative and add clouds in a sky above the snowman.

WRAPPING PAPER: (See *Crafts, printing potatoes.*)

WREATHS: Buy styrofoam wreaths (approximately 12-inches across). Buy several bags of gumdrops and plenty of toothpicks. Let residents cover the styrofoam forms with gumdrop candies by pushing a toothpick through each gumdrop into the styrofoam. When it is completely covered, add a bow at the bottom. Hang on the wall. (These are great decorations to hang over a decorated fireplace. They are very heavy.

Easter Crafts

EASTER BONNET: Give each resident a paper plate. Set out a selection of old bows and ribbons, artificial flowers, artificial fruit and lace. Help residents cut two slits directly across from each other, in their paper plate, about an inch in from the outside edge. Through these slits have them thread a wide funeral-type ribbon about a yard or so long. Pull it tight across the bottom of the paper plate so there are two long strings for ties. With this accomplished, let them staple and glue the decorations you have laid out onto the paper plate. Let your administrator judge the loveliest bonnet and offer a prize. Perhaps the ladies would like to put their bonnets on and have an early Easter parade through the facility.

EASTER EGG DECORATION, GIANT: You will need round balloons, approximately 10-12" and a large roll or two of heavy crochet thread. Blow up the balloons and tie them. Mix wallpaper paste (purchased at wall covering department or store) with water until it's the consistency of thick soup. Cut off about 20 yards of string and soak in this until it's drenched. (A heavy solution of sugar water may be substituted for the wallpaper paste but it is messier.) Begin to wrap string all around the balloon criss-crossing in no particular pattern until the balloon is thoroughly covered. Tie a piece of string to the mouth of the balloon and hang the balloon up to dry on a shower rod, clothesline or something similar.

When the paste on the balloon is dry and the string is hard, break the balloon by pricking it. Holding the string ball up on one end, cut out with scissors a circular window in the front of it. Remove the broken balloon pieces. Put Easter grass inside on the bottom. Then place a small bunny or similar decoration inside. Candy may be placed in it and the decoration becomes a unique Easter basket. Over the raw cut edges of the stringed decoration, hot glue pretty lace. This decoration may be hung or set up on a fashioned styrofoam base.

St. Patrick's Day Crafts

SHAMROCK: Cut large poster board patterns of shamrocks. Let residents trace around these on green construction paper and cut them out. Give them glue, glitter, sequins and whatever else you have on hand, and let them decorate their shamrocks. Display them all on a wall or a door.

Thanksgiving Crafts

TURKEYS, PRUNE: You'll need prunes, raisins, miniature marshmallows, gumdrops, toothpicks, and tiny muffin papers. Use a prune for the body and toothpicks for the legs. Half a toothpick makes a tail and the other half the neck. On the neck half, push several raisins to cover and attach to the prune. Add a tiny marshmallow for a head and a piece of red yarn for the waddle. Let residents push the muffin wrapper onto the tail toothpick and secure it with a raisin. Push the turkey's feet into two gumdrops.

TURKEY, LEAF: Collect several leaves. Give residents each a leaf and a piece of construction paper. Have them glue the leaf in the center of the paper for the turkey's body. Give them markers or crayons to draw the neck, head and legs. Give them strips of colored paper to make tail feathers and the feet.

Valentine's Day Crafts

VALENTINE PEOPLE: From red construction paper, have residents cut out several hearts in various sizes. Let them glue these hearts together to make people—a big heart for the body, slightly smaller one for the head, several small ones for the arms and legs. Provide yarn for hair and markers and scraps of black and white paper for eyes, nose, mouth. Residents may want to make paper aprons for lady dolls and moustaches for men dolls.

VALENTINE BOUQUET: Begin by painting as many flower pots as you wish to use. Gather felt, fabric (gingham is good), styrofoam, wire, ribbon and glue. Give residents small squares of poster board, each about 2-1/2-inches by 4-inches. Let them cut fabric and felt to the same size and glue it on both the front and back of the cardboard. (Some flowers will be made of felt, some of fabric.) When it dries, let residents trace a valentine on the square of fabric and cut it out. With a sharp point, press a hole, for them, at the bottom of each cardboard heart. This is where the flower stem is attached. Let residents glue rick-rack around the edge of their valentine flowers. Press a piece of styrofoam into the pot. Attach wire through the hole in the valentines for stems. Push several "flowers" into the styrofoam in the pot. Tie a ribbon around the pot.

VALENTINE BOX: This activity will cause residents to reminisce about their school days. Choose a large box, and let them paint it white, or cover it with tissue paper. Have each resident make valentines and glue some of them around the outside of the box. Put the rest inside. Give them scrap lace, ribbon, rick-rack, glue and glitter and let them make an old-time valentine box. Cut a slit in the top. Buy or make valentines to fill it.

Chapter 7

Cooking

BISCUIT MAKING: Many a homemaker of yesteryear was famous for her biscuits. She probably still has the knack. This can be limited to a small group of alert residents, but even low-functioning and confused ladies come to life, so to speak, when you give them some flour and shortening and a rolling pin. Those who don't take part in the making can certainly enjoy eating them.

Provide each resident with ingredients, a bowl, pastry blender or a fork to cut the shortening into the dough and a pan for her biscuits. Cover your tables with a plastic cloth or rolled paper or wax paper, and let them go to work. Here's an old recipe if residents need one.

Old-fashioned Biscuits

2 c. flour
3 tsp. sugar
2 tsp. baking powder
1 tsp. salt
1/2 tsp. soda
1/3 c. shortening
2/3 c. buttermilk or milk soured by adding 1 tsp. lemon juice.

Heat oven to 450. Measure flour, sugar, baking powder, salt and soda in a bowl. Cut in shortening thoroughly until mixture looks like meal. Stir in most of milk. If dough is too stiff to work, add just enough milk to make it soft, puffy and easy to roll. Gather scraps on lightly floured board (table). Knead dough about 1/2 minute. Roll about 1/4 inch thick. Cut with upside down floured glass or biscuit cutter. Place on ungreased baking sheet. Bake 10 to 12 minutes or until golden brown. Serve to residents with butter and jelly. This can also be a contest.

BUTTER MAKING: As many residents come from farm backgrounds, fresh butter is a real treat. Here's an easy way to please them.

Buy fresh sweet cream. Fill two or three small jars partially full with this and secure the lid. Set residents around a table and pass the jar around, letting each

Cooking

Cooking

one shake it until they are tired and then pass it to the next one. In a few minutes, you'll have fresh butter. Spread this on saltine crackers and enjoy the compliments. (This butter will not be bright yellow unless food coloring is added.)

CANDY MAKING: This can be done at Christmas time or throughout the year. For cooked candy, use a deep electric cooking pot. Do not allow residents to do the actual cooking as they could injure themselves or others. They may mix the ingredients before cooking or do any follow-up work such as rolling the candies in coconut or sugar. Here are a few easy recipes.

Reese Peanut Butter Cups

3 1/2 c. powdered sugar
1 1/3 c. graham cracker crumbs
2 sticks margarine
1 c. peanut butter
Mix together. Press into 9" by 13" inch pan.
Melt:
1/3 stick margarine
12 oz. chocolate chips (milk chocolate chips are best, we think.)

Pour this over mixture pressed in the pan. Refrigerate to cool. Cut in squares.

No-Cook Peanut Butter Fudge

Mix with fork and then hands:

1 c. peanut butter
1 c. honey
2 c. dry milk crystals

Pat in an 8" by 8" pan and cut in squares.

This fudge may also be varied by adding other ingredients such as oatmeal (you may have to add a little more honey or water if you add this) raisins, dates, coconut, nuts or sunflower seeds. Rather than put in a pan, it may be rolled in balls and then be rolled in coconut, powdered sugar or chopped nuts.

Peanut Butter Candy (Makes 16 pieces)

1 c. peanut butter
1 pkg. (12 oz.) butterscotch pieces
6 c. crisp rice cereal.

Melt peanut butter and butterscotch together in top of double boiler. Pour mixture over cereal in a bowl, stirring until cereal is evenly coated. Press mixture into a buttered 9" by 13" pan. Chill. Cut in squares.

Fool-Proof Fudge (Makes about 1-1/2 pounds)

3-6 oz. pkgs. semi-sweet chocolate morsels
1-14 oz. can Eagle Brand sweetened condensed milk (not evaporated
        milk)
Dash salt
1-1/2 tsp. vanilla extract
1/2 c. chopped nuts (optional)

In top of double boiler over boiling water, melt morsels with sweetened condensed milk. Remove from heat; stir in remaining ingredients. Spread evenly into wax paper-lined 8" square pan. Chill 2 hours or until set. Turn fudge onto cutting board. Peel off paper and cut into squares. Cover and store at room temperature.

Turtles (fast)

12 caramels
8 oz. semi-sweet chocolate or milk chocolate (use 1 oz. squares of baking
        chocolate or chips)
4 dz. pecan halves

Line a cookie sheet with wax paper. Arrange 48 pecan halves, flat side down in groups of 4 with ends meeting in center. Flatten 12 caramels to 1-1/2 inch squares. Place one in center of each group of pecans. Melt eight 1 oz. squares semisweet chocolate, stirring occasionally until smooth. Spoon over caramels, leaving nut tips showing. Let stand in a cool place until firm, about 1 hour. Store in refrigerator. Makes 12.

Fantasy Fudge

3 c. sugar
3/4 c. margarine (1-1/2 sticks)
5 oz. can evaporated milk (2/3 c.)
1-12 oz. pkg. chocolate chips
1-7 oz. jar marshmallow cream
1 tsp. vanilla

Combine sugar, margarine and milk in heavy saucepan. Bring to full rolling boil stirring constantly. Continue boiling five minutes over medium heat, stirring to keep from scorching. Remove from heat. Stir in chocolate until melted. Add marshmallow cream and vanilla. Cool at room temperature.

CHEESE BALL:

1 lb. natural cheddar cheese
1-1/2 c. walnuts
2 - 3 oz. pkg. cream cheese, softened
1/2 tsp. garlic powder
1 T. Worcestershire
2 T. instant minced onion
1 T. chili powder

Early on day of serving: Grind cheddar cheese with 1 cup walnuts. Blend in cream cheese, garlic powder, Worcestershire and minced onion. With hands, shape mixture into a large ball. Roll ball in chili powder then in additional walnuts until well coated. Refrigerate until firm. At serving time, arrange ball on serving dish with crackers and spreaders.

CHEESECAKE: Buy *Jello* or *Royal* packaged cheesecake. Let some residents make up the graham cracker crust, others mix the filling and others open cans of cherry pie filling. Prepare in the morning and serve for an afternoon special treat.

CINNAMON ROLLS: Buy frozen bread dough in the grocer's freezer case. Let thaw. You can also use canned biscuits rolled together as dough. Have on hand sugar, cinnamon, melted margarine and rolling pins. Cover a table with a plastic cloth and put flour on the cloth where each resident will work. Give each a ball of the bread dough and let them roll it out into a rectangular shape 1/4 inch thick. Have them spread this with melted margarine and then sprinkle it well with a mixture of cinnamon and sugar. Let them then roll it up, jelly-roll fashion, and then slice this into rolls about 3/4 inch thick. Arrange close together in 9" by 13" pans. Let rise in a warm place until double in bulk, perhaps an hour. Bake about 30 minutes at 350 degrees. Serve with coffee.

CINNAMON TOAST: Let residents toast bread and spread with butter. Let them prepare a cinnamon-sugar mixture and sprinkle on toast.

COOKIES: Some good cookie recipes follow.

No-Bake Cookies (These are really more of a candy.)

2 c. sugar
1/2 c. milk
1 stick margarine
4 T. cocoa
1/2 c. peanut butter
3 c. quick-cooking oats
1 tsp. vanilla

Boil sugar, milk, margarine and cocoa for 1-1/2 minutes. Start timing after mixture reaches a full, rolling boil. Remove from heat; add peanut butter, oats, and vanilla. Beat until blended, then drop on buttered waxed paper by teaspoonfuls. Coconut, chopped dates or raisins may be added if desired. These may be placed in the refrigerator to hasten hardening.

Preacher Cookies (These are unbaked and candy-like, too).

4 T cocoa
2 c. sugar
1 stick butter or margarine
1/2 c. nuts
1/2 c. milk
1 c. oatmeal
1 c. coconut (optional)

Boil sugar, milk and butter three minutes. Add remaining ingredients. Mix well. Drop onto buttered wax paper. If needed, add a little extra oatmeal.

Skillet Cookies (Quick, easy and delicious!)

1 8 oz. package chopped dates
1 stick butter or margarine
3/4 c. sugar
2 eggs, beaten
1 tsp. vanilla
Pinch salt
1 c. nuts
2 c. Rice Krispies
Coconut

Cook dates, butter, sugar, eggs, vanilla and salt in a skillet for ten minutes. Press dates against the sides of pan to mash. Add the nuts and Rice Krispies. Cool and form into small balls, the size of a walnut. Roll in coconut.

Rice Krispies Treats

4 c. miniature marshmallows
1/4 c. margarine
5 c. Rice Krispies

Melt margarine. Add marshmallows. Stir until melted. Cook three minutes longer. Remove from heat. Add cereal. Pat in 9" by 13" buttered pan. Cool. Cut in squares.

No-Bake Fruit Bars

1 c. raisins
1/2 c. almonds
1 c. assorted dried fruit
1/4 c. dry milk powder
1/4 c. graham cracker crumbs.

Chop fruit, nuts and add other ingredients. Roll in 1-inch balls. Store individually in plastic wrap or bags.

Rich Chocolate Cookie Bars

1/2 c. margarine
1-1/2 c. graham cracker crumbs
1-14 oz. can Eagle Brand sweetened condensed milk (not evaporated)
1 c. milk chocolate chips
1-1/2 c. coconut
1 c. chopped nuts

Preheat over to 350 degrees. In 9" by 13" pan, melt margarine in oven. Sprinkle crumbs over this. Pour sweetened condensed milk evenly over crumbs. Top with remaining ingredients and press down firmly. Bake 25-30 minutes. Cool. Cut in bars.

COOKIE ICING: Buy large sugar cookies and canned frosting, sprinkles and candies for decoration. Give residents each some cookies and let them see how creative they can be. Decorations can vary with the seasons.

DONUT FRY: This is a sure winner with everyone. Be sure to fry many extra because when the aroma of fresh donuts begins to permeate the facility, you'll have everyone checking out the activity room. Here's your chance to make some brownie points with staff who may be giving you a rough time.

Buy refrigerated biscuits in the can. Have some residents open them and place them on cookie sheets. Have other residents cut a hole in the center. Either use a donut cutter or the top of a salt shaker as a cutter. Put shortening or oil in a deep fryer or electric pot filling it about half to 2/3 full. Heat grease to 375 degrees. Donuts should be cooked two minutes, turning once. If it takes longer, your grease is not hot enough. If it takes less time, your grease is too hot, and the donuts will be dark on the outside and doughy on the inside. (Do NOT leave a resident in charge of this task. Either you, another staff member or a volunteer should do the actual frying of the donuts because of possible burns or accidents.)

Before you begin to fry, fill several small bowls with powdered sugar, sugar with cinnamon and icing. Have residents line trays or cookie sheets with several layers of paper towel. Fry the donuts and place them on paper towels. When cool enough to handle, let residents roll them in the sugars or ice them and stack them back on trays. It'll be difficult, but try to get residents to wait until the donuts are all fried and then serve hot coffee and fresh donuts. Residents enjoy helping to clean up the mess, too.

FRIED MUSH: This is another old favorite.

You can make the mush by cooking cornmeal and water. When thick, form into a roll. Let set overnight in the refrigerator. Next day, fry it on a griddle in the activity room. Rolled mush can also be purchased in the supermarket. Serve with molasses or syrup.

FRUIT SALAD: In summer when fruit is plentiful, purchase fresh cantaloupes, watermelon, peaches, pineapple, blueberries, bananas and strawberries. Have residents wash their hands and then cut up all the fruit and mix it together for a big fruit salad. Top with whipped cream and let them enjoy eating their creation.

GRANOLA: Granola is a treat residents can eat dry for a wholesome snack, and it is fun to mix.

> 1 c. honey
> 2/3 c. oil
> 2 tsp. vanilla
> 8 c. uncooked rolled oats
> 4 c. shredded coconut
> 2 c. walnuts (coarsely chopped)
> 1 c. instant dry milk powder (optional)
> 1 1/2 c. wheat germ (optional)
> 4 tsp. cinnamon
> 1 c. raisins
> 1-1/2 tsp. salt

In a small mixing bowl beat together till smooth and creamy, the honey, oil and vanilla. Set mixture aside. In large mixing bowl, stir together oats, coconut, nuts, wheat germ, milk powder salt and cinnamon. Pour the honey-oil mixture over dry ingredients and mix well first with a wooden spoon and then with hands. Spread into four 9" by 13" ungreased baking pans or two larger ones. Bake 350 degrees, 25 minutes, stirring three or four times during baking period. Watch closely and turn oven temperature down to 300 degrees if the granola starts turning a little too brown toward the end of baking period. Remove from oven. Add raisins and stir. Store in an air-tight container. Serve plain as a snack to be eaten with hands like popcorn or with fruit and milk. This is a very large batch.

HEAVENLY HASH:

> 1 c. sour cream
> 1 c. coconut
> 1 c. marshmallows
> 1 c. crushed sweetened pineapple
> 1 c. mandarin oranges
> Sweeten with sugar if desired.

Mix together. Can be served immediately, but better if refrigerated a few hours.

HOT DOG PARTY: Cook hot dogs and provide trimmings at each table. These might include: coney sauce, mustard, catsup, relish and onions. Give each resident a bun and allow them to make their own. Serve with root beer.

ICE CREAM: This brings back for residents memories of leisurely Sunday afternoons, special reunions and parties when everyone took their turn at cranking. The electric ice cream maker is far more convenient, but residents really enjoy having a share in making it in the traditional way. About 20 minutes of good turning usually produces ice cream. If you have enough residents and a volunteer, it's not difficult to do in this way. Here's a simple recipe:

Vanilla Ice Cream

> 4 cans of Milnot evaporated milk
> 2 c. sugar
> 1 T. vanilla
> 4 eggs, beaten with a fork

Mix well in ice cream freezer can. Put top on this and set in the base of the freezer. Pack a layer of ice between the can and the bucket. Sprinkle ice with ice cream salt, then pack another layer of ice, then sprinkle again with salt. Do this until the freezer is almost full of ice. Attach top of freezer and turn or plug in until finished.

Variations of this recipe: When ice cream is partially set, you can add fresh fruit like berries or peaches and then continue to freeze. Or, at the beginning when you mix the other ingredients, you may add instant pudding for flavoring. Reduce the vanilla if other flavorings are used.

JAM: Here's an easy recipe.

Strawberry-Rhubarb Jam

4 c. rhubarb (chopped in 1-inch pieces)
3 c. sugar
1-3 oz. pkg. strawberry jello

Cook diced rhubarb with sugar until done (10-15 minutes or less). Remove from heat. Add dry jello. Stir. Pour into jars and keep refrigerated. Great spread on toast or biscuits.

JELLO SALAD: This is an easy one for residents to mix. It can be served as a cool afternoon treat.

12 oz. frozen whipped cream
12 oz. cottage cheese
1-16 oz. can crushed pineapple
1 box dry lime or lemon jello

Mix together. Can be served immediately but better if refrigerated a few hours.

LUNCHES: Residents may want to have special lunches from time to time that they prepare themselves. Here are two suggestions:

Spaghetti

Purchase spaghetti and Ragu or other brand prepared sauce. For convenience, buy the kind with meat included in the sauce. Purchase frozen garlic bread that can just be heated and served.

Chipped Beef on Toast

Buy packaged dried beef in prepared meat section. Make a white gravy and then add the beef and heat. Serve over toast.

MUFFINS: Buy a prepared mix or let residents make their own. Here's a recipe for Blueberry Muffins.

Blueberry Muffins

3/4 c. Crisco
1-3/4 c. sugar
3 eggs
3 c. flour
3 tsp. baking powder
1-1/2 cup milk
pinch of salt
3 c. blueberries

Preheat oven to 375 degrees. Cream Crisco and sugar; add eggs. Sift dry ingredients together and add alternately with milk. Fold in berries. Fill greased muffin tins 2/3 full. Sprinkle tops with sugar. Bake 25 minutes. Makes 36 medium muffins

NOODLE MAKING: Mix up several batches of noodles and let residents roll them out and cut them; or let residents each mix their own recipe. Give them to the kitchen to cook for the next day's menu.

OYSTER SOUP: Cook up a pot of oyster soup and serve with tiny oyster crackers. A separate pot of potato soup can be prepared for those who do not like oyster soup.

PANCAKES AND SORGHUM MOLASSES: Before Mrs. Butterworth and modern syrup products, folks long ago relied on good old molasses for their pancakes. It's a real treat for them to have it again.

Gather two or three long griddles for frying pancakes and set them up in the activity or dining room. Use a pancake mix that requires only adding water. A resident or two might want to mix this. With supervision, a few alert residents might want to cook the pancakes. Serve with sorghum molasses. Check your supermarket for it.

PIE BAKING: This activity, for the most part, is for alert residents; but occasionally if you give a very confused lady a rolling pin and dough, you'll be very surprised how that person knows just what to do with it. She may just make a fine pie crust.

If fresh apple pies are to be made, earlier in the day have a few ladies peel and slice the apples. Make up pie dough in advance. Work with a manageable size group. Collect several rolling pins so each lady can have one. Give each a ball of dough and a pie pan. Provide apples, cinnamon and sugar within reach of each participant. Have table knives handy for them to split their top crust. Some may want to sprinkle sugar on the top crust. Others may want to rub milk over it. When finished, bake the pies. Serve later or the next day. This can provide two or three activity sessions with the apple peeling, pie making and the eating. It's fun to make this into a pie baking contest and have the administrator, DON or dietitian do the judging.

PIES, SIMPLE VERSION: Buy prepared pie crusts or let residents make them. Buy instant pudding (any flavor) and let residents mix with hand mixers. Pour into pie shell. Let set a few minutes. Let residents spread frozen whipping cream (thawed) on top. Prepare several and serve for afternoon snack or for a pie social. A good recipe follows:

Hershey Bar Pie

Crust:

>   3 cups corn flakes
>   1 T. sugar
>   1/4 c. melted margarine
>   pinch salt

Filling:

>   1/4 lb. (12) marshmallows
>   1/2 c. milk
>   6 Hershey Bars
>   1/2 pt. whipping cream

Mix together finely-rolled corn flakes, sugar, salt, and butter. Press into a 9-inch pie pan to form crust.

Melt marshmallows and Hershey bars in milk in double boiler. Cool. Whip cream and fold into cooled chocolate mixture. Pour into crust. Refrigerate. Best when made a day before serving. Garnish with whipped cream and maraschino cherries. Makes 8-10 servings.

PIE CRUST SNACK, OLD FASHIONED: Let residents mix up a batch of pie dough. This can be from scratch or a box. Let them roll the dough out to a large rectangle and put on a cookie sheet. Have them turn up the edges of the dough just a little. Next, spread this rolled pie dough with butter or margarine and then sprinkle this liberally with sugar, then cinnamon. Bake about 10 minutes at 350 degrees. The crust need not get brown to be done.

Break in pieces and let the residents eat it like a cookie.

PIZZAS, MINI: Though a popular food for some time, pizza is still not an every day food for many residents. Yet by making their own pizzas, they usually find they enjoy eating the food.

Buy refrigerated biscuits in a can, tomato paste or sauce, shredded pizza cheese, parmesan cheese and oregano. Let residents open the biscuits and each take one. Have them flatten their biscuit with their hands or a rolling pin until its twice its original size in diameter. Next, let them spread the paste or sauce on the biscuit and sprinkle it with parmesan cheese and oregano and then top it with a little pizza cheese. Bake 425 degrees about 10 to 12 minutes or until done. Serve with 7-Up or Coke.

Note: To save baking time, English muffins, split in half, may be used in place of refrigerated biscuits. Just heat until warm and the cheese melts. A microwave can be used for this if desired.

POTATO, BAKED: Provide trimmings at each table. These might include: sour cream, cut broccoli, cheese sauce, bacon bits and chili beans. Give each resident a large baked potato split in the middle. Allow residents to top their own potatoes. These extras on baked potatoes may be a new experience for them, so you may have to help them a little. Serve with milk to drink.

RHUBARB AND BISCUITS: This is another old-time food residents enjoy. Have residents open refrigerated biscuits and place on cookie sheets. Bake according to package directions. Next, have residents cut rhubarb up into one-inch pieces. Put it in an electric cooking pot and cover it with 2 cups of sugar or to sweetness desired. The rhubarb has much natural water in it which will cook out of it, so if you add water to cook the rhubarb, use very little. Cook it for ten or fifteen minutes or until soft. Add a box of strawberry jello for color and flavor. Spread on biscuits and serve to residents.

TAFFY PULL: Let everyone have a hand in pulling. You might want to pass out disposable rubber gloves for this purpose or pass around a bucket of soapy water for residents to wash their hands before you start. Here's one recipe.

> 2 T. butter
> 1/2 c. water
> 2 T. vinegar
> 2 c. sugar
> 1 tsp. vanilla

Melt butter, add water and bring to a boil. Stir sugar in carefully until all dissolved. Cook three to five minutes. Uncover and boil to 260 degrees. Pour onto a buttered plate and sprinkle on vanilla. When cool enough to handle, pull into pieces.

WINE MAKING: If your facility has no apprehensions about this, here's an easy recipe:

Locate a glass gallon jug with a small neck like root beer or cider come in.

> 2-12-ounce cans of frozen grape juice
> 1 T yeast
> 3 c. sugar
> A round balloon

Thaw the grape juice concentrate in a gallon pitcher. Add sugar and dry yeast. Fill the gallon pitcher with water. Mix well and pour into the small necked gallon jug. Stretch the balloon neck over the neck of the jug. With a needle, poke a small hole in the top of the balloon to let air escape as the juice becomes wine. The balloon will rise as the yeast works and will go down some near completion. In two weeks the wine should be ready to drink. Residents can do most of the mixing for this project. They may want to talk about the days of prohibition after making it. When completed after two weeks, serve with cheese and crackers.

Chapter 8

Word Games

Word Games are invaluable. They are great for residents who will not get physically involved in group activities. They help keep minds alert by recalling things learned long ago. They are an ice breaker and are great to entertain residents daily while they are waiting for their lunch to be served. But best of all, they can readily bail you out if your planned activity falls through at the last minute. Word games might include more than just word games as we think of them. Let's take a look at some successful thought provoking activities. Few are original. They have been around for a long time.

ANIMAL FUN: What do you call the babies of these animals?

Goat	Kid
Fox	Cub
Lion	Cub
Bear	Cub
Kangaroo	Joeys
Dog	Pup
Pig	Piglet
Sheep	Lamb
Cat	Kitten
Moose	Calf
Penguin	Chick
Heron	Egrets
Seal	Pup

WHAT NOISES DO THESE ANIMALS MAKE?

Snake	Goat	Cricket
Donkey	Cow	Chicken
Lion	Pig	Horse
Mouse	Oxen	Sheep
Eagle	Frog	Dog
Cat	Bear	Bird

Word Games

Word Games

VEHICLE QUIZ: See if residents can recognize these old-time slogans.

1) When cars are made better, ____ will make them. Buick
2) The auto with a reputation behind it. Studebaker
3) I love what you do for me. Toyoto
4) See the USA in a ____ Chevrolet.
5) The closer you get, the better we look. Ford
6) Look for the white triangle. Hudson
7) The mark of excellence. General Motors
8) A car worthy of its name. Rickenbacker
9) The world's champion auto. Dusenberg
10) The universal car. Ford
11) Watch the ____ go by. Ford's
12) Ask the man who owns one. Packard
13) Nothing runs like a deer. John Deere (tractors)

AUTO QUIZ:

1) What other old cars can you remember? Packard, Hupmobile, Moon, Franklin, Morman, Whippet, Peerless, Stanley Steamer, Haynes
2) What was a drawback of the Stanley Steamer? It took a long time to get the water hot, and then sometimes the steam engine would blow up.
3) Who invented the Model T? Henry Ford
4) How much did he pay his assembly line workers? $5.00 a day
5) From 1900 to 1915, what kind of car was considered a ladies car? Electric car

BIBLE QUIZ:

1) What was St. Paul's name before it was changed to Paul? Saul
2) Where was Paul's boyhood home? Tarsas
3) Was St. Paul one of the original twelve apostles? No
4) Where was Jesus born? Bethlehem
5) Which town did He live in as a boy? Nazareth
6) Who played his harp to soothe King Saul? David
7) Which creature was the first to leave the ark after the flood? Dove
8) What is the first book of the Bible? Genesis

9)   What is the last book of the Bible? Revelation
10)   Who wrote the four Gospels? Matthew, Mark, Luke and John
11)   Which book of the Bible is songs and poems of David's? Psalms
12)   Which book gives many wise sayings? Proverbs
13)   Which holiday celebrates Jesus rising from the dead? Easter
14)   How many apostles were there? 12
15)   Which apostle denied Jesus?   Peter
16)   Which one betrayed him to his captors? Judas
17)   How did Judas die? Hanged himself
18)   Who replaced Judas as an apostle? Matthias
19)   Which one is known as "the doubter?" Thomas
20)   What famous prayer did Jesus teach? Our Father

BIRD QUIZ: Give the definition and have residents fill in the blank and name the bird.

1)   An out building and to eat: Barn Swallow
2)   A bird representing peace: Dove
3)   Likes to sing: Canary
4)   A copycat: Mockingbird
5)   Likes to knock: Woodpecker
6)   Comes out at night: Owl
7)   A baseball team named after this bird: Oriole
8)   An unhappy bird and a letter: Blue Jay
9)   Official U.S. bird. Eagle
10)   A tool and what sits above one's shoulders: Hammerhead
11)   Steals the bank's money and a hotel: Robin
12)   Brings babies: Stork
13)   Catholic high official. Cardinal
14)   A huge machine to lift: Crane
15)   A dark color: Blackbird
16)   A little crazy: Cuckoo
17)   Not a singer but carries a tune: Hummingbird
18)   Lives in church steeples: Pigeons
19)   Name suggests a wintertime bird: Snowbird
20)   A fire and to leave: Flamingo

NAME AS MANY BIRDS AS YOU CAN: Here are some:

Bluebird	Cardinal	Sparrow
Wren	Wood Chuck	Peacock

Owls	Hammerhead	Pigeon
Canary	Snow bird	Nightingale
Dove	Cuckoo	Blackbird
Mockingbird	Oriole	Starling
Parrot	Parakeet	Quail
Pheasant	Flamingo	Sea Gull
Stork	Crane	Prairie-Chicken

COOKING: In this quiz, give the ingredients of a recipe and ask residents to tell what those ingredients will make. Here's an example:

Tomatoes, milk, butter, salt and pepper (tomato soup)
Sugar, cocoa, salt, milk, butter, vanilla (fudge)
Flour, baking powder, salt, shortening, water (biscuits)
Powdered sugar, butter, milk (icing)
Flour, shortening, salt, water (pie dough)
Meat fat, flour, water, salt and pepper (gravy)
Lemons, sugar, water (lemonade)

CURRENT EVENTS: Open the newspaper and choose subjects that might interest residents. Read titles and discuss articles. Ask residents how they feel about the information. Use the front page. Try *Ann Landers* or *Dear Abby*. Try some from the sports section.

DO YOU REMEMBER: Get old days books from the library or use a specially prepared reminiscent book with all the questions already prepared such as *Remembering the Good Old Days* or *Looking Back.* (See Reference.)

FLOWER NAMES: Name as many flowers as you can. Here are some:

Marigold	Violet
Bridal Wreath	Jonquil
Trumpet	Goldenrod
Tulips	Bachelor's Buttons
Poppy	Aster
Sweet William	Bouncing Betty
Rosemary	Ladies' Slippers
Jack-in-the-Pulpit	Elder

FOOD FUN:

1)   When the photographer wants you to smile, he tells you to say
     _____ (cheese).
2)   When cars are backed up for miles, you say it's a traffic _____(jam).
3)   The teacher says, "Use your _____ (noodle)."
4)   A nickname for New York City is the Big _____ (Apple).
5)   An embarrassed person turns as red as a _____(beet).
6)   George Washington's dad was furious when he cut down the_____ tree
     (cherry).
7)   Santa's belly shook like a bowl full of _____ (jelly).
8)   Someone who's easily scared might be called a _____ (chicken).
9)   When a person has a tender heart, he might be said to be as soft as a
     _____ (marshmallow).
10) Paper money is sometimes called _____ (lettuce).
11) When someone is skinny, you might say they look like a _____
     (stringbean).
12) If Cinderella wasn't home by midnight, she would turn into a _____
     (pumpkin).
13) If you run over a nail, your tire becomes as flat as a _____ (pancake).
14) If a prize fighter swings at you, you _____ (duck).
15) Likeable grandmothers might be said to be as sweet as _____ (pie).
16) To support one's family is called to bring home the _____ (bacon).
17) People with partial gray hair are said to have _____ hair. (salt and
     pepper)
18) Really bad fog might be said to be as thick as _____(pea soup).
19) When you know someone is stringing you along, you say,"That's a lot
     of_____ (baloney)".
20) Someone who's a real clown and likes to perform might be called a
     _____ (ham).
21) _____ is the staff of life. (Bread)
22) County fairs are as American as _____ (apple pie).
23) Identical twins are as alike as two _____ (peas in a pod).
24) Golfers _____ [tee (tea)] off.
25) A crowded football stadium packs spectators in like _____ (sardines).
26) Twins make a_____ [pair (pear)].
27) A fast runner might be said to be as fast as_____ lightning. (greased)
28) An unscrupulous young man might be said to be sowing his wild _____
     (oats).
29) A devoted, trustworthy person might be called the _____ of the earth.
     (salt)

30) When someone finds himself in trouble he might be said to be in a _____ (pickle).
31) When someone is worrying, he might be said to be in a _____ (stew).
32) A girl with lovely skin might be said to have a _____ complexion. (peaches and cream)
33) A gambler might be playing for high _____ [stakes (steaks)].
34) When one wants to savor an event, he _____ (relishes it).

HOLIDAYS: Go through each month and ask residents to name what holiday falls in that month. Ask, then, how many holidays they can name.

January:	New Years
January/February:	Chinese New Year
February:	Groundhog Day
	Valentine's Day
	Washington's Birthday
	Lincoln's Birthday
March:	St. Patrick's Day
	Mardi Gras (Fat Tuesday)
March/April:	Palm Sunday
	Good Friday
	Easter
April:	April Fool's
	Arbor Day
May:	May Day
	Memorial Day
	Mother's Day
May/June:	Ascension, Catholic Holy Day
June:	Confederate Memorial Day
	Father's Day
July:	Independence Day
August:	Assumption, Catholic Holy Day
	of the Blessed Virgin Mary
September:	Labor Day
September/October:	Rosh Hashanah or Jewish New Year
	Yom Kippur, Jewish Holy Day
October:	Halloween
	Columbus Day
November:	All Saints Day
	Thanksgiving
	Veterans Day

December: Pearl Harbor Day
                    Immaculate Conception, Catholic Holy Day
                    Christmas
                    Hanukkah, Jewish Holy Day

FAMOUS INVENTORS Who invented these?

Steamboat (1787):	Robert Fulton, Rumsey, Fitch, Stevens
Kodak Camera (1888):	George Eastman
Typewriter (1867):	Christopher Sholes
Cotton Gin (1793):	Eli Whitney
Electric Light (1810)	Thomas Edison and Sir Humphry Davy
The airplane (1903:	Orville and Wilbur Wright
Electromagnetic Telegraph	Samuel F. B. Morse
Telephone 1876:	Alexander Graham Bell
Television (1920)	VladimarK. Zworykin
Electronic Computer (1946	Dr. John Mauchly, J.Eckert Jr., J. G. Brainerd
Fountain Pen (1884)	Lewis Waterman
Safety Pin (1825)	Walter Hunt
Dirigible (1900)	Ferdinand von Zeppelin
Telescope (1608)	Hans Lippershey
Zipper (1893)	Whitcomb L. Judson
Victrola	Thomas Edison
Lightening Rod	Ben Franklin
Penicillin	Alexander Flemming
Repeating Rifle	Oliver Winchester
Radio	Marconi

JOKES AND RIDDLES: Collect these from the newspaper or books. Here are
a few:

1)   Who was the greatest actor in the Bible? Sampson. He brought down the
     house.
2)   What go up the stairs on their heads? Nails in your shoes.
3)   What tree is nearest the sea? Beech.
4)   Why did the dog try to bite his tail? He was trying to make ends meet.
5)   Why should a fish be well-educated? He lives in a school.

6)   What is the value of the moon? Four quarters
7)   What table has no legs? Mathematics table
8)   How do bees dispose of their honey? They cell it.
9)   What's the difference between a jeweler and a jailer? One sells watches, the other watches cells.
10)   Where did Noah strike the first nail on the ark? On the head
11)   Why did the boy drown in bed? The mattress slipped and he fell right into the spring.
12)   Why is 3 + 6 = 10 like your left foot? Because it's not right.
13)   Where do sheep get their hair cut? At the baa baa shop
14)   What side of the cat has the most fur? The outside
15)   What is the quietest sport? Bowling. You can hear a pin drop.
16)   What does everyone overlook? His nose
17)   What is the principal part of a horse? The mane part
18)   Who writes the most letters? Fishermen. They're always dropping a line.
19)   How do you keep an elephant from charging? You take away his charge cards.
20)   What did one wall say to the other? Meet you at the corner.
21)   When is a farmer cruel to his corn? When he pulls its ears
22)   How do you keep a mouse from squeaking? Oil it
23)   How many men are born in New York City every year? None, just babies are born there.
24)   If a skunk goes to church, where does he sit? In his own pew
25)   What goes up in the air white and comes down yellow and white? An egg
26)   Why is a barn so noisy? Because the cows have horns
27)   Why can't you tell secrets in a corn field? Because there are so many ears around
28)   What is the surest way to keep water from coming in your house? Don't pay your water bill.
29)   What kind of help is best for hotels? The inn-experienced
30)   Why do tall people rest more than short people? They lie in bed longer.

MATHEMATICS TABLES: You can buy mathematics table cards and ask the equation to residents (4 + 5 = —) and see which resident can answer first. By asking the equation to a group gathered around rather than to individuals, it encourages those who know the answer to speak up, yet prevents anyone from being embarrassed if they don't know the answer. Even though a resident may not speak out an answer, he is probably mentally trying to recall the answers thereby taking part right along with the other residents. If you have a resident who will not take part in any activities, try this one (and other word games) while they are in the dining room waiting for lunch. Often they can't resist the urge to let you know that they know the answer. Watch who seems to be interested and be sure to chart this as activity on their charts.

MEASUREMENTS:

How many cups in a quart?	4
How many ounces in a cup?	8
How many pounds in a ton?	2000
How many ounces in a pound?	16
How many pints in a quart?	2
How many cups in a pint?	2
How many inches in a foot?	12
How many feet in a yard?	3
How many inches in a yard?	36
How many feet in a mile?	5280

NURSERY RHYMES: Get a children's book of nursery rhymes and read a part of the rhyme and let residents finish it. Here are a few:

A Dillar, A Dollar

A Dillar a dollar,
A ten o'clock scholar
What makes you come so soon?
You used to come at ten o'clock
Now you come at noon.

Ding Dong Bell

Ding Dong Bell,
Pussy's in the well!
Who put her in?
Little Johnny Green.
Who pulled her out?
Big Johnny Stout.
What a naughty boy was that
To try to drown poor pussy cat,
Who never did him any harm,
But killed the mice in his father's barn.

Little Jack Horner

Little Jack Horner sat in a corner,
Eating his Christmas pie.
He put in his thumb, and took out a plum,
And said, "What a good boy am I!"

Georgie Porgie

Georgie Porgie, pudding and pie.
Kissed the girls and made them cry.
When the boys came out to play,
Georgie Porgie ran away.

Little Boy Blue

Little Boy Blue, come blow your horn,
The sheep's in the meadow, the cow's in the corn.
Where's the boy that looks after the sheep?
He's in the haystack, fast asleep.

The Old Woman Who Lived in a Shoe

There was an old woman who lived in a shoe;
She had so many children she didn't know what to do.
She gave them some broth, without any bread;
She whipped them all soundly and sent them to bed.

POETRY: Locate poems residents might remember and read them to them. Stop periodically and let them finish a line. You might select poems such as *Trees* or *The Village Blacksmith*.

PRESIDENTS QUIZ:

1) Who was the first president of the United States? Washington
2) What president taught himself to read? Lincoln
3) What man who later became president led the Rough Riders up San Juan Hill? Teddy Roosevelt

4)   Who was Teddy Roosevelt's daughter? Alice
5)   Do you remember anything about her? She was mischievous, sliding down banisters in front of dignitaries and carrying garter snakes in her purse among other things.
6)   Name two presidents who were Indian fighters? Zachary Taylor and William Henry Harrison
7)   What president died of pneumonia one month after taking office as a result of not wearing a hat while outside in cold weather giving his inaugural speech. William Henry Harrison
8)   Who was the first president to wear long pants in the White House? Thomas Jefferson
9)   Who was the last president to wear a beard? Benjamin Harrison
10)   What president was called Rough and Ready? Zachary Taylor
11)   What president is called the Father of our country? George Washington
12)   Did Harry Truman always live in the White House? No. During remodeling of the White House from 1948-52, he lived across the street in Blair House.
13)   What president purchased the Louisiana Territory? Thomas Jefferson
14)   Approximately how many rooms are in the White House? 100
15)   What are the three things required to be president?
            a) must be a citizen
            b) must be at least age 35
            c) must have been a resident of the U.S. for 14 years
16)   What president was a revolutionary soldier at age 13? Andrew Jackson
17)   Who was the only 20th century president without a college education? Harry Truman
18)   Who was the first divorced president? Ronald Reagan
19)   His election made him the Republican party's first president? Abraham Lincoln
20)   Who was known as the father of our Constitution? James Madison
21)   This president had a grandson who also became president. Who was he? William Henry Harrison
22)   He fought several duels to defend the honor of his beloved wife Rachel? Who was he? Andrew Jackson
23)   Who was your favorite president? (Most residents usually choose FDR.)
24)   How many presidents can you name?

PRESIDENTS' NAMES, PARTIES, STATES

| George Washington | Fed. | VA |
| John Adams | Fed. | MA |

Thomas Jefferson	Dem. Rep.	VA
James Madison	Dem. Rep.	VA
James Monroe	Dem. Rep.	VA
John Quincy Adams	Dem. Rep.	MA
Andrew Jackson	Dem.	SC
Martin Van Buren	Dem.	NY
William Henry Harrison	Whig	VA
John Tyler	Whig	VA
James Knox Polk	Dem	NC
Zachary Taylor	Whig	VA
Millard Fillmore	Whig	NY
Franklin Pierce	Dem	NH
James Buchanan	Dem	PA
Abraham Lincoln	Rep	KY
Andrew Johnson	* (see note)	NC
Ulysses Simpson Grant	Rep	OH
Rutherford B. Hayes	Rep	OH
James Abram Garfield	Rep	OH
Chester Alan Arthur	Rep	VT
Grover Cleveland	Dem	NJ
William McKinley	Rep	OH
Theodore Roosevelt	Rep	NY
William Taft	Rep	OH
Woodrow Wilson	Dem	VA
Warren Gamaliel Harding	Rep	OH
Calvin Coolidge	Rep	VT
Herbert Clark Hoover	Rep	IA
Franklin D. Roosevelt	Dem	NY
Harry S. Truman	Dem	MO
Dwight Eisenhower	Rep	TX
John F. Kennedy	Dem	MA
Lyndon B. Johnson	Dem	TX
Richard M. Nixon	Rep	CA
Gerald Ford	Rep	MI
James E. Carter, Jr.	Dem	GA
Ronald Reagan	Rep	CA
George Bush	Rep	ME
Bill Clinton	Dem	AR

* Andrew Johnson: A Democrat nominated Vice President by Republicans and elected with Lincoln.

PRODUCTS AND SLOGANS Do you remember any of them?

1) When it rains, it pours. (Morton Salt)
2) It floats. (Ivory Soap)
3) Leave the driving to us. (Greyhound Bus)
4) A little dab'll do you. (Brylcream)
5) Relief is just a swallow away. (Alka Seltzer)
6) Won't wear off as the day goes on. (Ban Deodorant)
7) You'll wonder where the yellow went. (Pepsodent Toothpaste)
8) Breakfast of champions. (Wheaties)
9) We try harder. (Avis Rent-a-car)
10) I'd walk a mile for a ___ (Camel Cigarette)
11) Stretch you coffee break. (Juicy Fruit Gum)
12) Hate that gray. Wash it away. (Lady Clairol)
13) Beer that made Milwaukee famous. (Schlitz)
14) 57 varieties. (Heinz)
15) You like it. It likes you. (7-Up)
16) Candy with the hole in it. (Lifesavers)
17) Tell them Charlie sent you. (Starkist Tuna)
18) From contented cows. (Carnation Milk)
19) Covers the earth. (Sherwin Williams)
20) Melts in your mouth, not in your hand. (M & M's)
21) Don't squeeze the _____ (Charmin Bath Tissue).
22) Look for the seal on the peel. (Chiquita Bananas)
23) ___ just keeps on ticking. (Timex)
24) Good to the last drop. (Maxwell House Coffee)
25) 99 and 44/100% pure. (Ivory Soap)
26) The soap of beautiful women. (Camay)
27) Beautiful hair doesn't have to cost a fortune. (Suave Shampoo)
28) How do you spell relief? (Rolaids)
29) Let your fingers do the walking. (Yellow Pages)
30) Everything's better with ___ on it. (Blue Bonnet Margarine)

PROVERBS: Read old proverbs to residents but do not give the ending of the proverb. Let them finish each one.

1)   Other men live to eat while I eat to: live
2)   A bird in the hand is worth two in the: bush
3)   Out of the frying pan into the: fire
4)   Practice makes: perfect
5)   As you make your bed, so you must: lie in it
6)   Don't throw a monkey-wrench into the: machinery
7)   Strike while the iron is: hot
8)   As large as life and twice as: natural
9)   All things come to him who: waits
10) Forty is the old age of youth. Fifty is the youth of: old age
11) Heaven helps the men who will not: act
12) Nothing to fear but: fear itself
13) Possession is nine tenths of the: law
14) Keep a stiff upper: lip
15) Actions speak louder than.: words
16) Brave actions never want a: trumpet
17) Leave well enough: alone
18) It's never too late to: learn
19) It will all come out in the: washing
20) A fool and his money will soon be at: debate
21) No sooner said than: done
22) It is a great ability to conceal ones: ability
23) It's never too late to: learn
24) Give me liberty or give me: death
25) You can't teach an old dog new: tricks
26) He that goes barefoot must not plant: thorns
27) Trouble runs off him like: water on a duck's back
28) What's sauce for the goose is sauce for the: gander
29) Early to bed, and early to rise makes a man: healthy, wealthy and wise
30) Cut off one's nose to spite one's: face
31) Live and: learn
32) Beauty is but: skin deep
33) Absence makes the heart grow: fonder
34) Out of sight, out of: mind
35) With tooth and: nail
36) April showers bring: May flowers
37) Make hay while the: sun shines
38) A wise son makes a glad: father
39) It is better to die on your feet than to live on your: knees

40)   Better to face a danger once than be always in: fear
41)   The day has eyes. The night has: ears
42)   Birds of a feather: flock together
43)   Never grieve over: spilled milk
44)   The early bird catches the: worm
45)   He makes no friend who never made a: foe
46)   He who pays the piper can call the: tune.
47)   We have all forgotten more than we: remember
48)   No man is free who is not master of: himself
49)   Genius is one percent inspiration and 99 percent: perspiration
50)   In war there are no: winners
51)   The wildest colts make the: best horses
52)   The big toad in a little: puddle
53)   Friends though absent are still: present
54)   Faint heart never won: fair lady
55)   A soft answer turns away: wrath

SIMILIES: Offer the residents the first three words and let them fill in the blank. Fat as a....(pig).

Hot as a firecracker	Pure as a lily
Tough as nails	Stubborn as a mule
Deep as the ocean	Untamed as a tiger
Fast as greased lightening	Wild as the wind
Sly as a fox	Playful as a kitten
Slippery as a greased pig	Dirty as mud
Neat as a pin	Fair as a flower
Sharp as a tack (nail)	Crazy as a loon
Clear as a glass (bell)	Swift as a deer
Thin as a stringbean	Bitter as gall (persimmons)
Cold as ice	High as the heavens
Stiff as a board	Red as scarlet
Soft as velvet	Sour as a lemon
Sneaky as a cat	Clean as a whistle
Flat as a pancake	Blue as the sky
Ugly as sin	Green as grass
Pretty as a picture	Poor as a church mouse
Slippery as an eel	Spry as a spring chicken
Dead as a doornail	Still as a mouse
Strong as an ox	Tight as a drum

High as the sky
Proud as a peacock

Sick as a dog
Hungry as a bear

SIMPLE SPORTS QUIZ:

1) What do you call it when you score in football? Touchdown
2) How many points do you get for a basket in basketball? 2
3) How many points for a free throw in basketball? 1
4) How many points do you get for a touchdown in football? 6
5) How do you get extra points in football? Kick ball over or run through the goal posts.
6) What do you call a score in bowling when all the pins are down? Strike
7) How many bowling pins are there in all? 10
8) Name some positions on a football team? Quarterback, fullback, half-back, lineman, guard, running back
9) Name some positions on a basketball team. Center, forward, guard.
10) What's the gentlest of all sports? Tennis because you score with love
11) What sport do you play with a bat and a ball? Baseball
12) How many players are on a baseball team? 9
13) Who is the Home Run King? Babe Ruth
14) What game starts by jumping for a ball? Basketball
15) What game starts with blowing a whistle and a kick off? Football and soccer
16) How many players are on a football team? 11
17) Who was the famous coach of Notre Dame? Knute Rockne
18) What is the nickname of the Purdue team? Boilermakers
19) How do you score in baseball? Get a run
20) How do you score in basketball? Put a ball through a hoop
21) What sport requires wearing knee-length pants? Football, baseball

SONG TITLES: Fill in the blanks.

I'll See You in My _____ (Dreams)
Singing in the _____ (Rain)
Alexander's _____ (Ragtime Band)
My _____ Stood Still (Heart)
The _____ Strutters Ball (Darktown)
Down by the Old _____ (Mill Stream)
Sleepy _____ (Time Gal)
I'm Forever _____ (Blowing Bubbles)

Tip Toe Through the _____ (Tulips)
Let Me Call You _____ (Sweetheart)
My Wild Irish _____ (Rose)
When You Wore a_____(Tulip)
There's a Long, Long_____(Trail)
St. Louis_____(Blues)
Back Home Again in _____(Indiana)
Some of These_____(Days)
April_____(Showers)
My_____Baby (Melancholy)
By the Light of the_____(Silvery Moon)

TOGETHERNESS: On these, simply give the residents the first item such
as bread and.... and let them fill in the blank (butter) .

Lost and found	Hit and run
Rough and ready	Mother and Father
Salt and pepper	Spot and Puff
Hammer and nails	Dog and cat
Knife and fork	Fair and warmer
Ham and eggs	Nuts and bolts
Pork and beans	Gold and silver
Ice cream and cake	Love and hate
Coffee and tea	Live and die
Soap and water	Heaven and hell
Towel and wash cloth	Safe and sound
Day and night	Cap and gown
Light and dark	Stocks and bonds
Cup and saucer	Stars and stripes
Rich and poor	Past and future
Pure and simple	House and home
Hope and pray	Work and play
Gift and giver	Crackers and cheese
Bow and arrow	Butter and bread
Horse and buggy	Macaroni and cheese
Coat and hat	Peter and Paul
Collar and tie	Tom and Jerry
Shoes and socks	See and hear
You and me	Drunk and sober

STATE ABBREVIATIONS: (old and new versions)

1) Which state is part of the leg? NE
2) Which state takes care of the bills? PA
3) Which state is self-centered? ME
4) Which state is happy? GA
5) Which state is a flour used in making bread? RI
6) Which state is an unmarried girl? MISS
7) Which state is a surprised exclamation? OH
8) Which state cuts long grass? MO
9) Which state is curious? WY
10) Which state is very clean? WASH
11) Which state processes food? KAN
12) Which state is an animal doctor? VT
13) Which state is a hotel? IN
14) Which state is friendly? HI
15) Which state rescued Noah and his family? ARK
16) Which state tastes bad? AK
17) Which state is a number? TENN
18) Which state is inclusive? AL
19) Which state is just alright? OK
20) Which state is to trick someone? CONN
21) Which state is a former president's first name? CAL
22) Which state is in error? FLA
23) Which state is the opposite of women? MINN

STATES AND CAPITALS

Alabama: Montgomery	Delaware: Dover
Alaska: Juneau:	Florida: Tallahassee
Arizona: Phoenix	Georgia: Atlanta
Arkansas: Little Rock	Hawaii: Honolulu
California: Sacramento	Idaho: Boise
Colorado: Denver	Illinois: Springfield
Connecticut: Hartford	Indiana: Indianapolis

Iowa: Des Moines	North Carolina: Raleigh
Kansas: Topeka	North Dakota: Bismarck
Kentucky: Frankfort	Ohio: Columbus
Louisiana: Baton Rouge	Oklahoma: Oklahoma City
Maine: Augusta	Oregon: Salem
Maryland: Annapolis	Pennsylvania: Harrisburg
Massachusetts: Boston	Rhode Island: Providence
Michigan: Lansing	South Carolina: Columbia
Minnesota: St. Paul	South Dakota: Pierre
Mississippi: Jackson	Tennessee: Nashville
Missouri: Jefferson City	Texas: Austin
Montana: Helena	Utah: Salt Lake City
Nebraska: Lincoln	Vermont: Montpelier
Nevada: Carson City	Virginia: Richmond
New Hampshire: Concord	Washington: Olympia
New Jersey: Trenton	West Virginia: Charleston
New Mexico: Santa Fe	Wisconsin: Madison
New York: Albany	Wyoming: Cheyenne

SUPERSTITIONS: Many old time superstitions are still with us. Ask residents if they know how these superstitions started.

1) Fear of black cats crossing in front of you...supposedly a sign of bad luck. In the middle ages, people thought the black cat was a companion of witches and that after seven years, it would turn into a witch.

2) Having Bridesmaids... In middle ages there was fear the bride would be kidnapped so she surrounded herself with bridesmaids who dressed exactly like her to confuse the kidnapper.

3) Throwing an old shoe after a bride...Opinions differ but the custom may go back to Bible times when a shoe was taken off and given to confirm a sale or exchange. Women were considered property.

4) Drinking toasts... goes back to the Romans when a young man would drink as many glasses or toasts as letters in the name of his mistress.

5) Bells tolling the dead... This ancient custom, seldom heard of today, was used to call Christians to pray and also to scare away or delay the evil spirits from getting to the body.

6) Rabbits foot... supposedly brings good luck. It developed because primitive men were impressed with how rabbits hopped with their hind legs and seemed to thump the ground sounding like someone was speaking.

7) Throwing a pinch of salt over one's shoulder...supposedly a power of protection. This was to bribe evil spirits who planned to harm you.

8) Walking under a ladder... In Asia long ago, criminals were hung from the seventh rung of a ladder. Death was thought to be contagious so the practice was feared.

9) Knock on wood... People long ago would ask a favor of the tree god and when it was granted, they would knock on the tree to say thank you.

10) Brides wearing a veil...This practice was so evil spirits wouldn't see her face and know who she was.

11) Saying "God bless you"...People used to think evil spirits jumped out when one sneezed and by saying this, they were protecting themselves.

12) Ship christening is an ancient custom where a heathen priest would bring an egg and some brimstone and dedicate the ship to the god whose image it bore.

TIMES AND SEASONS:

1) Name the months of a year? Jan. Feb. Mar. Apr. May June July Aug. Sept. Oct. Nov. Dec.
2) What year was America discovered? 1492
3) How many days in a year? 365
4) How many days in a leap year? 366
5) What is the shortest month? February
6) How many hours in a day? 24
7) How many weeks in a year? 52
8) How many months in a year? 12
9) Name as many holidays as you can? **New Year's**, Valentine's Day, St. Patrick's Day, Easter, Mother's Day, Father's Day, 4th of July, Labor Lay, Halloween, Thanksgiving, Christmas
10) When does spring start? March 21
11) Name the four seasons? Spring, Summer, Winter, Fall
12) Name as many kinds of trees as you can. oak, poplar, maple, elm, sycamore, pine, fruit

13) Name five oceans.   Atlantic, Pacific, Indian, Arctic, Antarctic
14) How many continents are there? 7
15) Name the continents? North America, South America, Europe, Asia, Africa, Australia, Antarctica
16) Which continent do you live on? North America
17) How many rivers can you name? Mississippi, Rhine, Nile, Hudson, Wabash, Ohio
18) When do you plant potatoes? Good Friday

Outings

*

Guests

*

Fill-ins

Outings
*
Guests
*
Fill-ins

Chapter 9

Outings

Many residents enjoy getting out of the facility for a little while. It also can make a nice break for you, the activity director, as you're surrounded in the facility by more work than you can handle. But where, you might ask, can you take your residents? Here are a few tried and true suggestions.

ANIMAL SHELTER: Call your animal shelter and ask if you can bring residents for a tour.

ANTIQUE STORE: Visiting an antique store for residents is like a trip back to their childhood and the early days of their marriage. They enjoy looking at furniture, household products and farm tools like they once used. This helps them to remember where they have been and to see how life has changed.

ART GALLERY: Some residents really appreciate good art; others are open to new experiences. Watch your newspaper for art shows, or call your local art museums or the Chamber of Commerce to locate showings.

AUCTION SALE: Determine beforehand whether this is just a window shopping spree or if residents are prepared to buy. If they want to buy, see if they have money available. If not, perhaps their families will provide funds for the event. You will probably want to arrive early enough for residents to browse. Take along lawn chairs so residents can sit back and relax. You might want to pack some sandwiches or snacks. Depending on the health of the residents, one to three hours will probably be as long as they'll want to stay.

BALL GAME: Any type of ball game—baseball, football, basketball, hockey or soccer will do. Check ahead for easy access and workable seating.

BOAT RIDE: Take residents for a ride on a large river boat. You may want to join with several other facilities in your area and reserve a boat just for residents. Lunch can be served on the boat. They will enjoy the leisurely float down the river.

BUS RIDE: Why not take your residents on a bus ride about town? It's possible that your city bus company will send a special bus to your facility at no cost, to provide your residents with an enjoyable afternoon. Contact your newspaper and the television station for publicity. Knowing a story is coming might just help the bus company decide to offer free rides. Even if you have to pay for the ride, it's an afternoon residents will long remember.

CIRCUS: When residents were children the circus was about the biggest event that could come to town. When a circus comes to your town, take a few residents and let them enjoy it once again. Even if they can stay only for a few acts, it's still a worthwhile trip. Make arrangements beforehand for handicapped seating.

COUNTRY DRIVE: Try to locate things in your area that still reflect an era long ago. For instance: a windmill, an outdoor pump, an old buggy, an outhouse, old barns and old farm equipment. Take residents out and let them get a close look at the items that were once so much a part of their life.

COVERED BRIDGE: There are still a few of them around. If there's a covered bridge near you, residents would enjoy such a trip as it will bring back many memories. Ask them about waiting out storms under them, or parking in their buggies there with their dates who often stole kisses. Take along a picnic or snacks.

CHURCH TOUR: Since most churches are kept locked today, arrange with pastors in your area for residents to visit their churches on a given afternoon. Let them leisurely look about the inside of the churches and take time to say a prayer, if they like, before moving on to another one.

DOG SHOW: Most towns offer dog shows at the local park or the fairgrounds. Take along lawn chairs and let residents enjoy the pets and reminisce about dogs they once had.

FAIR: In residents' day the county fair was one of the annual event they looked forward to. Take a group of residents and let them look at the animals and the farm equipment. They'll love discussing how farming has changed. Let the ladies enjoy the food, sewing, furniture and craft exhibits. Tour the midway, and let them delight in looking at the carnival booths and the rides. Buy them popcorn or corn on the cob (if they can eat it).

FARM: Many residents come from farm backgrounds so this will be a winner with them—especially the men. Arrange with a farmer for residents to visit his farm. Tour the barn, look at the stock, check out the fields and the garden. Perhaps you can arrange for the farmer's wife to serve a little refreshment in the house.

FIRE STATION TOUR: Call ahead and schedule a tour. Residents will enjoy seeing the fire engines and telling the firemen about bucket brigades and when horses pulled the fire wagons.

FISHING TRIP: Residents thoroughly enjoy this one. Just getting outside for a few hours is a special treat for them. Arrange a suitable place where it is easily accessible for wheelchairs. If your budget will allow, a paid private lake is usually very accommodating. There's a good possibility the owners of the lake will let your residents fish free, or at least offer you a discount.

Take plenty of volunteers along—one for every two people is not too many. Residents' families are a good place to start looking for fishermen volunteers who don't mind putting on worms or taking off fish. If at all possible, take some nurses aides along to help residents to the bathroom. And it's especially nice if you can get your administrator to come along. Its good for the residents to see him or her in a more relaxed setting where they feel free to talk with him/her.

Borrow fishing poles or buy inexpensive cane ones. At a fishing store, you can sometimes purchase them for about $5.00 apiece. Take a picnic lunch along— something simple that will require little work from you, because you will have your hands full with many details.

If you can, take along someone who plays a guitar or fiddle and can provide a little entertainment after lunch. You need not stay long, two or three hours is adequate. If the residents catch fish, have your fishermen volunteers clean them, and ask the kitchen to fry them up for supper.

GARAGE SALE: Everyone loves a bargain, even nursing home residents. Many may never have attended a garage sale, but it won't take them long to get in the swing. They'll probably be worn out after a half a dozen sales, but no doubt, they will want to go again. This might become a monthly event.

HAYRIDE: This is an activity residents will really like though you must be careful to select residents whom you can trust on a wagon. Arrange with a farmer to take residents on an afternoon hayride. Choose a low wagon with sides so residents won't fall off. They may want to set up lawn chairs in it. Watch your residents become children again as they play in the hay and reminisce of days gone by.

HORSE SHOW: For many residents, horses played a major part in their early lives. Locate a horse show and take residents. Arrange beforehand for accessible seating.

JAIL VISIT: Call ahead and schedule a visit at the county jail. Let residents tell how the jails have changed in their lifetime.

LIBRARY: You might tour the library with your residents and show them how the library has changed over the years. If there's a card file, show that to them. If a computer index is used, demonstrate the use of it. Ask them to suggest a book they once read and see if you can locate it. Tour the children's department with them. Let them see how toys play a part in getting youngsters involved in using the library. Let them browse through the periodical room. Help select a few books to use in your activity program or just for residents to look at.

MOVIE: Though residents can see videos at your facility, it's still a special treat to go to a theatre and see the large screen. You may even get a theatre owner to give a free showing or at least special rates for the residents to view a matinee.

MUSEUM: Most cities have at least one museum. Your residents will enjoy looking at the historical displays. They may well see things they personally remember using. If your museum has a small store inside it, why not check it out for publications about local history. You can take these back to your facility and use for reminiscing with residents.

NATURE TOUR: Take residents to an area where they might locate various items: acorns, leaves, pine cones, rocks and bark. Let them gather items, and then take these back to your facility where they can discuss their trip and their findings with residents who were unable to go.

NEWSPAPER: Arrange to tour your local newspaper and watch just how it is printed and put together.

OUT TO EAT: Residents enjoy this activity. If you call ahead, no doubt, you'll be met at the door and treated royally. Fast food places are usually slow in the early afternoons and are usually happy to welcome your residents. Don't be surprised if a resident orders a drink. Be sure to check on this before you go.

PARADE: In nice weather, take residents to a parade such as a Memorial Day or 4th of July parade. Provide lawn chairs for them to sit and watch.

PARK PICNIC: The park played a big part in recreation long ago and was also the scene of much courting. Take your residents, and let them leisurely stroll as they are able. Watch the swimmers, look at the animals, enjoy the children and rest in a swing under a big tree. You might take a picnic lunch. Later on, buy them a treat of cotton candy or an ice cream cone (if diets permit). They'll love you for taking them.

PIZZA PARLOR: Arrange to visit a pizza parlor and watch the pizza being prepared. Then, let residents feast on pizza and cold drinks.

POLICE STATION TOUR: Again, call ahead and schedule this one. Let the police tell how a person is booked and show how they are fingerprinted. Let them demonstrate the use of computers in police work. Ask to see a police car. Allow residents to ask questions.

RIDE ABOUT TOWN OR IN THE COUNTRY: This can be a very special treat. Residents like to look at old buildings they remember and see the changes. They can reminisce about the past. It's wise to take them by old schools and through the downtown. Discuss the long established businesses. In the spring, residents enjoy seeing the new leaves and the early flowers. In the summer, residents appreciate a trip to the country where they can look at the crops. In the fall, a trip through the country is relished because of the colors. Use your facility van or contact your local bus company. They may donate a free ride to residents during slow hours.

SCHOOL, GRADE SCHOOL: School has definitely changed since residents went, but it's worthwhile to orient them to the changes. Call a principal and see if your residents can visit the school, most probably in a specific class. Plan ahead what activity you can do together. In a young class, you might have residents and students compete in a spelling bee. It would be wise to mix teams including both the elderly and the students on each team. Many residents can well remember their states and capitals. You might spend some time before the school visit reviewing these with your residents before   tackling them with the children.

If the class is a little older, visit their history class, and let residents tell students about the Great Depression, farming and cooking long ago, old-time doctoring and health remedies. Let them talk about the dances they did, how they traveled, and the schools they attended. Let them tell about President Franklin Roosevelt and Harry Truman. They will be a hit with all the kids. This can become a regular monthly event.

SCHOOL, HIGH SCHOOL: Here's a fun activity if you have any residents who once attended the local high school. Schools generally preserve a copy of each class's yearbook. Find out the years your residents graduated, then call the school and make sure they have those years. Arrange with the yearbook advisor (usually a teacher) to bring your residents to visit the class where the new yearbook is being prepared. Let residents find themselves in the old books and share with the teacher and students about the changes in school and fashion since then. Be sure to call your T.V. station or your newspaper. This is a good human interest story.

SENIOR CENTER: Let residents make new friends and share in the center's activities such as bingo, movies, crafts and cards. In return, invite seniors at the senior center to your facility for lunch and activities another day.

SHOPPING: Even if residents don't have money to buy, they'll enjoy strolling through a K-Mart or the mall. Choose a time when stores are not crowded. Weekday mornings are good. Take along enough volunteers to help push wheel chairs or just keep an eye on residents.

STRAWBERRY FARM: Take along residents who are able to bend fairly easily, and let them pick berries. Blueberries are easier to pick and require less bending. When you return to the facility, let residents clean the berries. They can either eat them with other residents or pass them to the kitchen to be served as strawberry shortcake or blueberry muffins.

SUPERMARKET: Take your residents on a tour of a supermarket. Shop for an upcoming cooking project, and let them help you select items. Show them how prices are no longer stamped on most items and discuss how you find out what an item costs. Compare prices today with prices they paid. Explain the use of the scanner. Let them watch the butcher cut meat (if allowed). Show the new products that have come out in recent years. Ask how shopping differed when they were younger. This trip can certainly help orient residents to the reality of today's world.

TRAIN RIDE: If the Amtrack or a similar passenger line runs near you, why not take your residents on a short excursion to another city? Stop there for lunch and perhaps a sight or two, and then return home— or if getting residents off the train for touring is too much of a hassle, the train ride alone is a great opportunity for residents to have a change of scene.

WADING: On a warm sunny afternoon, you might want to take residents wading in a very shallow creek. They will relish taking their shoes off and wetting their feet in the water. Take along a few towels. If you live near the coast, residents would enjoy a trip to the ocean and wading near the beach.

Chapter 10

Guests

ANTIQUE COLLECTOR: Ask someone who loves antiques to bring easily transported ones to your facility and show them to residents. They might want to include things residents used in their early lives: shoe buttoners, churns, wash boards, cooking utensils and shaving mugs.

ARTIST: Invite artists who will demonstrate their work, both finished and in progress. Perhaps they will bring an easel and demonstrate how a picture is created. Don't overlook other measures of art such as pottery, wood crafting and jewelry making.

ARTHUR MURRAY DANCERS: Some dance studios will send out two professional dancers who will demonstrate ballroom dancing for half an hour or so for residents. Residents thoroughly enjoy recalling the dances of the past like the *Charleston* and the *Fox Trot*.

BATON TWIRLER: Contact schools or a local university band or your YWCA for names. Depending on the skill of the twirler, you may want to hold this event outdoors if the baton will be thrown high.

CAKE DECORATOR: Invite in a professional cake decorator, and let her demonstrate how to ice and decorate a cake. She may show how to make various kinds of flowers or the construction that goes into a wedding cake. Ask her to bring pictures of cakes she has made. Perhaps she'll even give samples to residents.

CHOIRS: High school choirs are great, as well as church and civic ones.

CLOWN VISIT: Most every city or town has at least one clown. If you can't find one, call your Chamber of Commerce, YMCA, Parks Department or your library to inquire. When the clown arrives, he may provide all his own entertainment, or you can have a ball and basket or bucket set out to play basketball with him or her. Have the clown visit the bedside of residents.

CRAFT DEMONSTRATION: Craft media are too broad to name, so you have an unlimited supply of people here. Contact a craft store and ask for a demonstration of various crafts. Contact individuals who like crafts and have them bring their finished crafts as well as demonstrate how they were made.

COLOR ANALYZING: Ladies love to look their best, even when they are in their 70's, 80's and 90's. Invite in a person who does color analysis, who drapes women with scarves to see which color looks best on them, and then puts make-up on them. During this activity, arrange for men to watch a football game on T.V. or a movie so you will not have to entertain them.

DIETICIAN: Invite to activities, your dietician, and have her demonstrate cooking something for residents to sample. She may want to talk a little about nutrition.

DOLL SHOW: Locate someone in your area who is a doll collector, and invite her to show her collection to residents. She can set the dolls up first for display and then, one by one, tell a little about each doll. Perhaps she will allow residents to handle the dolls and get a closer look. Most female residents love dolls, so this is usually a highly successful activity.

FAST FOOD RESTAURANTS: Though areas of the country might have different policies, fast food establishments will often visit facilities under the guise of public relations. In fact, they frequently have a community relations person in charge of this. Some who have come in the past in Indiana are *McDonald's* who held bingo monthly providing prizes and refreshments and *Hardee's* who alternated between bingo and making biscuits. *Pizza Hut* opened their facility to five or six residents monthly and served them free pizza and drinks.

FIREMAN VISIT: You might invite residents to attend the facility's annual fire inservice. They can watch the firemen demonstrate the use of a fire extinguisher and hear him teach on fire safety.

You can also invite a firemen in to talk to residents about his job. He may bring a truck for residents to view and let them hear the siren. He might bring a fire dog if the station has one. Allow time for residents to ask questions.

GUITAR, FIDDLE OR BANJO PLAYERS: Either individually or as a group, this type of music is always a big hit with residents. Those from farm backgrounds well remember the old-time barn dances and the fiddle and banjo music. This activity will even stimulate the very confused resident.

JUGGLER: It may take a little looking, but you'll probably be able to locate a juggler. Residents will enjoy this because it will remind them of the circus they used to attend.

LIBRARY: Contact your children's librarian and ask if they'd hold a regularly scheduled story hour at your facility. Gather residents in chairs in a large circle and place the children on the floor in the middle of the circle. This might take place during a specified reading week. This interaction might warrant your facility press coverage.

MEN'S LUNCHEON: (See *Men Only.*)

PETS: Do you have a zoo in your area? Does your local park have animals? Will your local animal shelter bring pets for residents to pet and hold? Will a local pet store bring pets to your facility? If so, you have the makings of a successful activity.

PHOTOGRAPHER: Ask a photographer to come and demonstrate how a camera works and what goes into making good pictures. He could demonstrate lighting techniques and how to choose a suitable background. Perhaps he would take some photos of residents.

POLICEMAN VISIT: Invite a policeman to visit residents and tell about his job. Perhaps he will bring a police dog and give a demonstration to residents how the dog obeys commands and helps in police work. Have the policeman show his car to the residents and demonstrate the radio, lights and siren.

POLITICIANS: This may not sound very interesting, but before elections, they are willing to come and talk to residents. Surprisingly, residents feel important that a person running for office would seek them out. Invite them to have lunch with residents. This can be considered current events as the politician alerts them to current issues in their town, state or country.

PUBLIC SERVICE: Your local public service sometimes has a community representative who will do demonstrations of products they sell such as a microwave oven. This is something residents did not use and are interested in.

SLIDE SHOW: Locate a local traveler, and ask him to show slides of his trips to various places. Have him talk about them. This is the next best thing to a vacation for residents.

SCHOOL KIDS: (See *Project, Adopt a Class*)

SENIOR CITIZENS TO LUNCH: (See *Outings, Senior Center*)

SQUARE DANCERS: These are usually a sure winner with residents. Contact a square dance club in your area, and invite them in for an evening. Most work during the day so it would probably be difficult to get them then. Residents will usually sit quietly for an hour and a half watching square dancing since so many of them used to dance in a similar manner. These can be invited in conjunction with a resident/family party. In this case, you might serve a meal first, and then have the dancers entertain. Invite the dancers for dinner.

WOOD WORKERS: Contact a retired carpenter or someone who enjoys working with wood. Ask him to give a demonstration.

WRESTLERS: This may sound like a strange activity, but it is highly enjoyed by residents. Contact your local high school wrestling coach and ask if he will allow some wrestlers to demonstrate for your residents. The wrestlers can bring their own mats. You have only to line residents up in a huge circle around the mats and watch them wrestle. The two-minute rounds seem like an eternity when someone is pinned down, but residents love the excitement. This is especially good for men, even confused or seldom involved ones. It would also be great entertainment for a stag party.

WRITER: Invite established writers, and ask them to tell a little about the life of a writer. Ask them to bring samples of their work.

Chapter 11

Fill-ins

Your calendar's almost planned, but you still have a few empty days that need to be filled; or your scheduled activity falls through; or you find yourself with bored residents on your hands. Perhaps you just need to fill your weekend calendar and can't think of anything that requires little preparation. Here's a few good fill-ins.

APPLE TASTING: Purchase various kinds of apples and cut them up. Let residents sample the different flavors. Ask them to guess which kind of apple they are eating. Read to them about Johnny Appleseed. Discuss ways of using apples. Discuss making apple butter the old-fashioned way.

BIRD FEEDING: Have the kitchen save the scrap toast from breakfast trays and any other old bread. If that is not acceptable, buy old bread at a bread store and dry it. Let residents break the bread up for the birds. You might also try making suet balls. Purchase suet from the supermarket meat department, grind it and mix it with bird seed. Then let residents roll it in tiny balls and tie them up in a mesh bag like onions come in. These bags can be hung from a tree outside the window.

BIRD WATCHING: In warm weather take residents outside and let them enjoy watching birds and other small animals. In winter, pull them up to the window where bird feeders have been hung and let them enjoy the tiny creatures. Putting ears of field corn out encourages squirrels to come also.

CLOWN VISIT: See *Guests, Clown Visit*

COUPON CLIPPING: Encourage staff and visitors to drop off recent magazines that they have already read. Stores often tear the cover off and then discard unsold magazines. See if they will give them to you. Also, save the coupon section from the Sunday paper. Gather residents and have them clip coupons.

These can then be left in a prominent place to be taken by anyone who desires.

CURRENT EVENTS: (See *Any Day.*)

FLOWER ARRANGING: Provide small vases and have a few ladies arrange flowers donated by funeral homes into small vases to set on tables in the dining room.

FOOT SWIM: In the middle of the activity room, fill a child's small plastic pool with warm water. Encourage residents to take off their shoes and go for a foot swim.

GREEN BEAN BREAKING: (See *Community.*)

GREETING CARD CUTTING: People are always giving greeting cards to health care facilities. Save them. Residents can spend literally hours cutting the backs off them and cutting out the pretty front section. You may want to have residents make door name tags for you by stapling to the edge of a 3" X 5" card pictures they've cut from the cards. All you have to do is write residents'names on these.

HAPPY HOUR: (See *Wine and Cheese* below.)

ICE CREAM SOCIAL: Keep a couple gallons of ice cream in the freezer and a new can of chocolate syrup and strawberry syrup in your activity cupboard. When you need a fill-in, break out the ice cream and make sundaes. Popsicles are also great to keep on hand.

MUSIC APPRECIATION: Put on good music and let the residents enjoy listening.

MOVIES: Video movies are always a good stand-by. You can put one on and do something else, or a staff member from another department or even a resident can easily put one on when you are not available. This can help you out evenings and weekends when you're not available.

MOVIES, HOME: If you or someone in your facility has old home movies and an 8-mm projector, bring them in and show residents. Home movies are often about someone's children growing up, but residents seem to enjoy kids whoever they belong to.

(The building where Comfort Retirement & Nursing Home in Lafayette, Indiana is located was built in 1929. One afternoon residents there were treated to a unique old black and white home movie. In it they saw the destruction of the former building on the site of their nursing home as well as the actual building of their present facility. Everyone laughed at the primitive building modes of the 20's and the backbreaking labor required before modern equipment. It was a great fill-in.)

NEWSPAPER READING: Gather residents together and spread out the day's newspaper giving a section to each person. Encourage them to tell you what's in the news. Have someone read major headlines and another person read the funnies to everyone and someone else the sports page.

NUT CRACKING: In season, have volunteers gather walnuts and other nuts that have fallen to the ground. Keep these in your activity cupboard. On a day you need a fill-in, get out the nuts, crack them, and let residents pick them. Package the nut meats and sell them to staff or save them for candy making.

PET THERAPY: If you find yourself in a pinch, call someone nearby and ask to borrow their dog or cat for an hour. Let residents enjoy the pet at their leisure.

PHOTO SHARING: Ask all residents who have photo albums to bring them to the activity room and share them with other residents.

PIE SOCIAL, MINI: Buy several pies, both frozen cream and the ready-to-bake fruit varieties. When ready, let residents have their choice. Don't forget the ice cream. Be sure to have an alternate treat for diabetics.

PLANT CARE: Have residents who are able care for the facility's plants, with supervision, of course. Residents like to pull off dead leaves, water and replant. Simply spread plastic or newspaper on the tables and let them go to work.

POPCORN PARTY: When you are stuck for an activity or when residents seem bored or restless, just put on the popcorn popper and watch them all come to life.

PUZZLE, JIGSAW: (See *Games.*)

RADIO, OLD TIME: Play tapes of old radio shows like *Jack Benny* or *Amos and Andy* or *The Shadow Knows*.

RECORDS: Collect old records—those big 78's from the 1930's and 40's. Ask family members. They may well be stored in a corner of their attics collecting dust. Also check with used furniture and junk stores; you may well get them for very little money. Residents enjoy just looking at the titles and remembering them. To play them, you may well have to dig up an older-style record player that plays that speed. Residents thoroughly enjoy an afternoon of listening to the nasal voice of Rudy Vallee and crooning style of Frank Sinatra. When the Charleston is played, they might even attempt to dance.

REMINISCENCE GROUP: When your entertainment doesn't show up, gather your residents around a large table and have a *Do You Remember* session (See *Any Day*).

RIBBON WINDING: Teach residents to wind the wide funeral ribbons around their fingers and secure them with a paper clip. This makes it easy for you to store many colors in a shoe box.

SHOE POLISHING: Provide polish and rags, and let residents polish their shoes and those of others unable to do their own.

SHOW AND TELL: Ask each resident to bring to the activity room a personal item that means something special to them. Have them tell about what they brought.

SING-A-LONG: Put on an a tape of songs of long ago and let residents sing along. Perhaps you or a resident can play the piano, a guitar or an accordion. The residents will love it.

SOCIAL HOUR: This is a good fill-in for evenings and week-ends. Have someone gather a group, large or small, into an area or around a table. Offer coffee or juice, and let residents socialize and visit among themselves. You can provide magazines, newspapers, puzzles, checkers, scrabble, dominoes and cards if you wish, but no doubt they'd rather just talk.

STUFF ENVELOPES: Whether it is your newsletter or a mailing, alert residents like to help with this job. Do it assembly line fashion, with residents being responsible for only one task at a time—folding, labeling, sorting, or putting on stamps. Otherwise you might have mass confusion.

WALK: Weather and volunteers permitting, take residents out for a short walk around the facility. In winter, form a train of residents and take a walk within the facility. You can make this more fun by featuring a scavenger hunt of pictures hung on walls for which residents are to keep a watch out.

WINE AND CHEESE: After your regular working hours when you still need to provide evening activities, this is a good one—if you can get the cooperation of your kitchen staff. After they have finished cleaning up the supper dishes, ask them to serve wine, beer and small cubes of cheese (that you have prepared beforehand) to residents still remaining in the dining room. Buy disposable clear glasses so there will be no real clean-up involved.

WORD GAMES: These are easy and fun. They can be used every day while waiting for lunch or in a pinch when you need fast activity. (See *Word Games*.)

YARN WINDING: Have residents wind skeins of yarn into balls.

Chapter 12

Projects

Sometimes it's helpful to get residents working on projects that take longer than a single activity session. This gives residents something to look forward to, plan for, work on, check on, and think about. It also builds comradeship among residents. Here's some projects that have been tried and tested on nursing home residents with positive results.

ADOPT A BABY: This is one residents really like. First, you need to find someone who has a baby or who is going to have one, and who likes to interact with the elderly. This could be a staff member or one of your own family members. You might want to advertise in the paper under "volunteers wanted."

Once you have your candidate, invite her to your facility. Have all the residents gathered together, and introduce the baby and his or her mother to the residents. Let some of them hold the baby. Also, take the baby to the room-bound, and introduce him or her. Plan a schedule when residents can expect to see their baby so they can watch it grow and develop. Take lots of pictures and keep them posted. Keep a chart with weight, height and all the new things baby learns between each visit. Let residents help select occasional gifts. Sometimes, provide a balloon or animal cookies (with the mother's permission, of course.) Encourage interaction between residents and the baby. Have residents sign special occasion cards for the baby's special days.

ADOPT A GRANDPARENT: Most all A.D.'s are familiar with this program so it needs little direction. It's usually carried out with a school class adopting your residents and each child choosing or being assigned to one resident. They get together regularly and form a friendship. Personally, I do not like this program for a simple reason. Seniors in nursing homes die, and dealing with death and the loss of their "grandparent" is difficult for some children. I feel that the following way is better for the children involved.

ADOPT A CLASS: It's fun to adopt a school class as a whole, and let them adopt

Projects
*
Community Involvement
*
Christmas

Projects
*
Community
*
Christmas

your residents. Any age works, but very special relationships can develop when a first grade class and your residents team up. Have the class visit one day each month, and plan an activity between the two generations. Some good ones might be a basketball game, bowling, coloring together, doing a craft, dyeing Easter eggs or watching a kiddie's movie together. Be sure to serve popcorn.

Personal attachments will indeed form, but encourage *all* the children to visit *all* the residents so many new friends are made. That way, when a resident dies, the children may indeed be sad, but it's not their *special* person, so they are not left without an adopted grandparent. It's really nice to work with the same teacher month after month, year after year in making this class adoption extra special.

ADOPT A PET: Having a pet at your facility can certainly bring some low-functioning residents to life, so to speak. Yet few facilities allow a dog or cat to make its home there permanently. The next best thing is to adopt a pet. It can belong to you, a friend who enjoys intermingling with the elderly or a park or zoo. Arrange for it to visit your residents on a regular basis so they can learn to love it. If possible, on its visits, let it stay a good portion of a work day so your facility becomes like a second home to the animal. It's especially beneficial to locate the pet in its infancy or youth so it can grow up knowing your facility and its special people. This pays big dividends for residents.

APPLE BUTTER MAKING: This is a major project so be sure you want to put the effort into it before you begin. If so, take some residents to an orchard with you, and buy a couple bushels of apples (Macintosh apples work well). Let able residents peel them, but don't worry about coring them if you have a food mill. The old-fashioned way is to use a copper kettle, cooking it outside for maybe six hours over an open fire. It must be stirred regularly. A wooden paddle is what residents once used to stir the delicacy. Check a hardware store for one, or just use a clean board.

A rough recipe goes something like this: Cook about two bushels of apples about three hours and then add approximately 25 pounds of sugar, a gallon of cider and two pounds of red hot candies (optional). Before adding the sugar, first dissolve it in another gallon of cider to prevent its scorching. When the sauce has become darkened and thick some people like to add cinnamon oil which can be purchased at the drugstore.

Note: If attempting this project, you may want to search out a recipe with more thorough directions.

A scaled down version of this project could certainly be held. Cook up just a small batch of applesauce inside over a small stove or hot plate. It can also be made in the oven using a heavy pan and stirring occasionally. Cooking time is about three hours.

ARBOR DAY: Arbor day is an annual tree-planting day set aside in most states to assist in foresting or reforesting scantily wooded areas, or in shading and beautifying cities and towns. It began in the 19th century. In most northern states, Arbor day is held in April or May; in Arizona, Texas and Alabama, it is held in February; In Florida, January; in Georgia, December; in New Mexico, March; and in West Virginia, both in spring and fall. It is often held in connection with the public schools to impress children with the importance of conservation.

Let residents help plant a tree, either on your facility grounds or in conjunction with a school class wherever they might select. Ask residents to tell you about Arbor Day when they were children in school. Ask them to recall any trees they planted throughout their lives and also any trees that hold a special significance to them—like ones on which they climbed or swung.

BABY PICTURE GUESS: Collect a baby picture of as many residents as you can. Check with their families for these. Post these pictures on a main bulletin board in your facility that is highly visible. Assign each picture a number. Put large letters above the pictures spelling "Guess Who". Provide a ballet box and a pencil, and let everyone guess who each baby is. Let this contest continue for a few weeks giving residents, staff and visitors a chance to vote. Offer a prize to the winner.

You can do the same thing with staff members' baby pictures, and this is often a fun activity. Gather pictures of the administrator, DON, A.D., head of housekeeping, food service supervisor and others who care for residents. Let residents have a part in guessing.

BAZAAR: If your facility is one that does crafts, quilting, sewing and ceramics, you may want to hold a big bazaar each year to sell your items. This may be held in November to help others get a head start on Christmas shopping. Advertise well on the radio and in the newspaper using free spots.

COFFEE KLATCH: Let lady residents take turns being the hostess. When it's her turn, let that resident invite in two or three friends from the community or from the facility. Set up a card table in her room and cover it with a nice cloth. Add flowers as a centerpiece. Serve simple, but nice refreshments.

COOKBOOK: Begin with your residents. Ask them for favorite recipes they still remember. Some recipes may include "a little of this and a little of that." That's alright since many used to cook that way. (You may want to try out some that sound questionable.) Send letters to families of residents and ask them to mail you their special recipes. As an incentive, offer a free cookbook in a drawing to one family member who provides a recipe. Ask staff to donate their favorite recipes too. Invite your cook to share some facility specials. Collect as many as you can.

If you hope to market your book for profit, there are cookbook publishers who will put the book together for you. If you just want to do it as a facility project, you can produce it yourself. The advantage of this is that you can make as few, or as many as you desire, and more as needed.

First, decide on the size of your book. You might want to take an 8-1/2" by 11" sheet of typing paper, and fold it in half. It will be 5-1/2" by 8-1/2". This is an economical size as far as copies go. Decide on any extra items you want to include—some tips from your residents on cooking, an old, old recipe or old helpful hints. Design a cover.

If you want your book to look professionally done, rather than typing on the actual paper, type your recipes into a computer using a word processing program. Then put them on a disk. Take this disc to a computing center, and have them "computer typeset" it. They can print the originals out on a laser printer. If you want to skip this step and simply type your recipes to fit the size of your pages. Either way, at this point, have a copy shop duplicate your pages and make up your books. Spiral binding works well. Prices vary, but the finished book will probably cost you $4 to $6 (mid-west prices) to produce depending on the size and the number of books made. Sell these books to staff and visitors, and advertise their sale elsewhere. Maybe a school your facility works with will help with the sale.

If you are not interested in making cookbooks to sell, you might produce a small one with all the recipes your residents use in their activity program and ones they might like to try. Have just a few books made at the copy shop to keep at your facility. Let residents use them when planning their next cooking project.

DOLL MAKING, SOCK: Help residents make these dolls from boys crew socks that have the colored stripe band on the top. Be sure to buy the ones with heels, not tube socks. The heel (in one sock) becomes the doll's bottom, and this sock becomes the basic body and legs of the doll. The other sock is cut off just under the ribbing. Cut this ribbing that you just cut off in two again (lengthwise). These two striped ribbed pieces will become the arms. (Save the foot section you cut off that sock for another project. You can save them up and crochet around the tops and have footies for residents.) Have residents hand sew each of these two ribbed arm pieces up the rough side and along the finished end (top of the sock). Leave the rough end open. Have residents stuff these as the doll's two arms. These will later be sewn to the body.

Now take the first sock that will be the body and legs. Turn it so the heel is in the back for a buttocks. The toe of the sock will be the head. Cut up the middle of the ribbing to where it joins the sock. This will create the two legs (still attached to the body). Turn the sock inside out and have residents sew up both legs but leave a little space at the crotch open for stuffing. Turn and stuff the legs and the body. Sew the crotch.

Now grasp what will be the head. Have someone who's adept at sewing, gather a row of stitching around the stuffed stocking, down a few inches from the top to create a neck. Sew around it a couple times for strength. Sew the stuffed arms to the body down a little from the neck. You will probably want to do, or at least supervise, the making of the face. Embroidery or use a permanent marker, and fashion two tiny upside down half moons for sleeping baby eyes. Make a tiny dot for the nose and a small red line for a mouth. Draw or embroider faint eyebrows. Cut out, and let residents sew small flannelette baby gowns and bonnets. Attach tiny satin ribbons for ties.

These dolls are machine washable and wonderful to give to underprivileged children at Christmas, to give as prizes for baby contests or to sell to staff and others to make money for other activity projects.

DOLL MAKING, APPLE HEAD: For exact directions go to the children's section of the library and locate a craft book on making apple head dolls. It takes a while, but they are not that difficult. Allow residents who are able to handle a knife to peel the apples, being sure to leave the stems intact. Let them cut slits in the apple for what will be the eyes and mouth. Cut lines for a simple nose. Cut other slits for wrinkles. Hang the apples by the stem where they can dry, possibly in front of a window catching sun. This will take a few weeks probably.

Distinct features will form as they dry. Meanwhile shape the bodies by bending wire to fashion a neck, arms, body and legs. This wire is wrapped with cotton that is tied on with string. If desired, tiny hands can be purchased at a craft store. For lady dolls, fashion white hair from cotton tied up in a little bun. Give grandpa dolls white hair also. Make glasses for them from wire. Cover their crude bodies with old-fashioned type doll clothes—a granny dress and apron for the lady doll and overalls for Grandpa. Make simple shoes from soft leather scraps. The finished dolls are darling if set in simple small rocking chairs like the ones made from clothespins. These will be highly saleable—if you can part with them. They last indefinitely though the face (apple) turns almost black in time.

DOLL HOUSE: Have someone build you a three-story Barbie doll house about 3 feet high, 3 or 4 feet long and 18-inches deep. Scrounge up scrap wallpaper, carpet, linoleum and fabric, and use this to decorate the house shell. Have residents make curtains by hand, and use dowel rods or new pencils for curtain rods. Some residents might crochet throw rugs and doilies while others may fashion bed spreads from fabric. Have them use tiny jewelry-type box lids for picture frames, and glue minature pictures cut from magazines inside them. Hang these on the walls. Use caps from dish washing soap for lamp shades. Attach a dowel rod to this, and slip it into a spool for the base of the lamp. Spray paint this gold. Make wastebaskets and planters from plastic lids that come on various products.

Visit a lumber yard, and get from their scrap box 2 by 4's to make couches and chairs. Cover them with foam and then fabric using a heavy-duty staple gun. Nail the pieces together with big nails. Make tables by using three spools glued together as the base. Glue a big peanut butter jar lid to the top. Stools can be made the same way, using one spool and a baby food jar lid. Have residents paint these. Decorate the house as you like. You will probably want to include a nursery. You may have to buy a small cradle and baby furniture. Continue to use odds and ends for furniture and accessories.

Make flower boxes at the base of the windows from tiny boxes glued on the outside. Make a white picket fence from painted popsicle sticks and glue it around the house. When the house is completed, buy a family of Barbie dolls to move in. This house may be given away in a drawing or kept for residents to enjoy. It's a wonderful way to bring your facility publicity at Christmas time. Announce it widely (through the press and schools), and have kids come in and sign up for a chance to win it. Hold a drawing sometime before Christmas.

GARAGE SALE: Work with nursing, housekeeping and maintenance to gather unwanted items that have collected around your facility: clothes, vases, knick knacks, extra walkers, whatever. Ask families and staff to donate toward your sale. Don't forget the crafts made by residents (if they can part with them). Advertise, and then set up shop, outdoors if weather permits or inside if not.

Be sure to include a bake sale, and ask the staff to contribute. Beforehand have residents bake and freeze cookies and candies for the sale. Then the day of the sale simply take them out and wrap them attractively in small packages. You can use the money made from this sale to support a big activity project or to buy a large supply of new bingo prizes.

HATCH CHICKS: If things seem to be slow around your facility, everybody seems in a ho-hum mood and residents seem less interested in activities, here's a sure pick-me-up. Try hatching baby chicks. As the new life prepares to emerge from the egg, it seems that new life is somehow generated into the residents and staff as they wait in anticipation for that first crack in one of the eggs.

It's easy to dismiss this one as being something too big for you, or to use the excuse that you know nothing about hatching chicks, but you can do it, and fairly easily, if you wish. Here's how:

This should be done when it's fairly warm outside, like in spring. Sometimes you can borrow an incubator from a chicken hatchery or a college or university that has a poultry department. This makes your job just a little easier. But if you can't locate one, don't give up the idea. It's easy to make your own incubator.

Locate a large cardboard box. Take a yardstick and measure the size of the bottom of the box. Go to a hardware store and buy a piece of chicken wire that is made up of tiny squares (approximately 1/4"). Have them cut you a piece of it that is 2" larger all around than the bottom of your cardboard box. If you have a friendly maintenance man or a helpful husband, let him do the next step. If not, it's not too difficult. Take a straight edge like a yardstick and a pair of pliers. Lay your straight edge two inches from the edge of your wire, and with the pliers, bend the edges up all along that side of the chicken wire. Do the same on all four sides until you have a box-like effect. Slip this into the bottom of your box as a raised floor for the eggs to rest on and for the chicks to walk on when they hatch. Beneath this wire, of course, is the bottom of the box which should be lined with aluminum foil. This will allow any spilled food, water or chicken droppings (and there are very few at first until you begin to feed them) to drop from where the chicks walk and where some unhatched eggs probably remain.

Your next step in constructing the incubator is to locate an old picture frame with glass that is as near the size of the front of the box as you can find. Slip this into your box along one side. It will be the viewing window. Next, cut away the front of the box. You want to keep the box from having too many air leaks, or you will be unable to maintain the needed temperature. You may have to use duct tape to attach the picture frame. Short of having a frame, a large piece of glass could be used if you secured it well with duct tape.

A dish or pie pan of water must remain in the incubator because the eggs need moisture to hatch. You will need to keep a thermometer in the box at all times to regulate the temperature. If it varies too much, your eggs may not hatch. It should remain between 98^0 and 101^0. A light bulb provides the heat. Locate an extension cord with a light bulb in a wire casing. This is to hang inside the incubator and remain on at all times. You would not want to have a fire hazard, so be very careful how you hang the light bulb. Keep it away from the cardboard sides. You may even want to line the areas near where it hangs with aluminum foil. The light has to be hung high enough so that the chicks, when they hatch, will not get burnt, yet not too near the top of the box. You'll have to experiment with the various size light bulbs until you find the one that will hold your temperature steady. Do not make the box totally air tight so some heat can escape.

Your next step is to locate fertile eggs. Check with a poultry house or a farmer who raises chickens. It takes about three weeks for the eggs to hatch. I've found it easier on the residents' patience to have the farmer incubate the eggs the first two weeks and then very carefully bring them to the facility. For the move, pack them tenderly, covered in a cloth, in a styrofoam cooler.

Don't get too anxious when you see the first crack in an egg indicating they are trying to hatch. Occasionally they come quickly, but usually it is hours or even a day before the actual hatching. Resist the urge to help the chick out of the egg because this pecking out helps the chick become strong. The hatched chicks survive well in the incubator for a couple of days, right along with the yet unhatched eggs.

Be sure to keep a saucer of water available for them to drink. This is not the same water (under the wire floor) that is used for humidity. Buy some chicken feed at a feed store. A five-pound bag will probably be more than you will need. A poultry expert claims the chicks do not need food for a day or two, just water, but they will begin to eat if it's offered right away.

A word of caution: When you remove your chicks from the incubator to a box, the facility will likely be too cold for them—especially if the air conditioning is on. Keep the box they remain in covered, and you may even need a source of heat such as a light bulb. This does not have to remain at 100°, though, like the incubator. In a day or two residents can begin to hold the chicks for a short time. Be prepared. It's very likely not all your eggs will hatch. Give them a few extra days just in case before destroying them.

Ducks can be hatched in the same way, and they seem heartier and more easily handled than chicks because they are larger. The ducklings will soon follow you down the hall as if you were a mother duck. Take them along as you make rounds. This provides great activity for bedside and low-functioning residents who are usually shocked, then awed to see a duck walking down the hall. Unfortunately, being larger, ducks are a little more messy than the chicks. Carry a tissue with you when you go walking.

One day before the ducks leave the facility, gather residents in the activity room. Fill a tiny plastic swimming pool or a large plastic container like a dish pan with warm water and let the ducks have their first swim. The residents will enjoy watching the event.

Be sure before you begin this project, to decide what will happen to your chicks or ducks after they've hatched and been at your facility for a few days. Probably the farmer who gave you the fertilized eggs will take them back. Generally some staff members want them. If so, make sure they live in the country and can take care of them once the newness wears off.

Hatching chicks can quickly become an exciting yearly event.

HUG DAY: Everyone needs a good hug. This is especially nice on Valentine's Day. Give each resident who wants to take part a large red construction paper heart. All day long he or she is to ask someone for a hug. Whenever they get a hug they have that person sign their heart. Whichever resident has the most signatures at the end of the day is the winner. He or she receives a hug from the administrator as well as a prize.

Some residents are too shy to ask for a hug. In that case, change your focus and give all staff members a bag of red paper hearts at the beginning of their shift. They are to sign their names on each heart. Each time they give a hug to a resident, they are to give the resident a heart. He or she will then put it in a special bag attached to his or her chair or clothing. At the end of the day the hearts will be collected and the staff member whose name appears the most is the winner.

KITE FLYING: (See *Monthly Biggies*)

MOVIE MAKING: This can be done in two ways. The first is to use a video camera or a 8 mm or Super 8 mm movie camera and take movies of the residents in action in various projects about the facility. There could also be interviews with residents.

The second way is to hold a simple play complete with costumes with residents as actors. When your movie is made, present it as a surprise to residents' families at a nice resident/family dinner. Also let the residents watch it from time to time.

NOODLE PROJECT: Some of your residents are good cooks. Others can follow directions. Once a month or so, let them make up noodle dough, roll it out, and then cut and dry the noodles. These can then be weighed and packaged in zip-lock bags and sold to staff and families of residents to make money for the activity department or for residents' outings (if your state or facility has no objection).

PEN PALS: Team up with a teacher and school class. Arrange for part of their English program to be the regular writing of letters to your residents. Perhaps a few of your residents can answer letters they receive, but more than likely, most won't be able to. If that's the case, write a group letter regularly with you gathering the quotes and thoughts on residents' hearts and putting them on paper. The teacher can read this letter to her class. Also, send some of the residents' art work, and encourage the teacher to mail the children's creative art to your facility so you can display it in your hallways for residents to enjoy.

PINEWOOD DERBY: Cub Scouts, year after year, hold a *Pinewood Derby* in which they are given a small block of wood and a set of wheels. They and their dads are supposed to create a car from these items which will race in the Pinewood Derby. A small track is set up. Contact a scout master, and see if he will hold his derby in your facility with residents cheering the winner on.

PLANT HOSPITAL: (See *Community Involvement*)

PRODUCE A PLAY: Make it a simple play, perhaps using a favorite childhood story or fairy tale. From this, write simple lines, but expect residents to *ad lib*. Residents can help make scenery using end rolls from newspaper print often given free upon request from a newspaper. This can be done in conjunction with a group of children such as scouts or a church group. Preparing for the play can fill several activity sessions. Let those not participating watch, and invite families of residents. Be sure each actor/resident takes a bow and gets a good applause. Serve refreshments when finished.

TELEPHONE ENJOYMENT: Arrange with a local school to carry out this project. Third, fourth and fifth grades work well. Match up one student with each of your residents. On a given day each week, accept a specific number of calls from your special school class. Gather your residents who will be receiving calls that day into the activity room or wherever a phone is available. For many residents, this will be the only call they have received in years, and it is greatly relished. Strong friendships develop as children are matched with their special elderly person by phone regularly.

TOY REFINISHING: About September advertise in free public service announcement spots, that your facility would like to collect good used toys to refurbish for needy children at Christmas—also that you would accept tiny baby clothes in which to dress the dolls. Decide which residents want to take part and set regular times each week for working on the toys. The ladies might bathe dolls and brush their hair. Others might sew, crochet or knit clothes for them. Some might dress other dolls in the donated baby clothes. The men can repaint or touch up trucks and cars, fix loose wheels and oil parts if needed. Residents can scrub or brush fairly clean stuffed animals and tie new ribbons around their necks. (Funeral bouquet ribbons are great here, and at no cost to you.)

The toys can be donated to individual families or to a community center or the Salvation Army for distribution by them.

WRITING CONTEST: Give residents who are interested, a topic and ask them to write on that subject. The topic could be: "what my home as a child looked like" or "what I remember about my early school days," or "the Great Depression and how it affected my life." Contact your local newspaper beforehand, and ask if the winner's entry could be published. If it's a large paper, and they are not interested, see if they will run the entry in "Letters to the Editor." Chances are they would be happy to not only run the article, but to cover your contest as well.

Chapter 13

Community Involvement

ARBOR DAY, PLANT A TREE: (See *Projects.*)

BASKETBALL: (See *Games.*)

BABY GOWNS: These can be made in number by residents who like to sew. The gowns can then be given to needy babies in the Third World or to a local hospital maternity department. It's especially nice to make the gowns in a Christmas flannenette print and donate them during the Christmas season. One can be given to each baby born at the hospital during that time.

Buy a pattern, or cut out a simple baby gown pattern from brown paper. One yard will make about three tiny gowns, two nice size ones. Sew the side and shoulder seams on a machine and let residents hem the arms, neck and bottom. Attach lace trim around the neck and tiny ribbon for ties.

BABY LOVING DAY: (See *Monthly Biggies.*)

BREAK GREEN BEANS: In season, offer a service to your community. Let interested residents break green beans and shuck corn for local people. These people may want to drop their produce off on their way to work and pick it up on their way home.

BRIDAL SHOW: (See *Monthly Biggies.*)

CELEBRITY DAY: (See *Monthly Biggies.*)

COMFORT GIVE-AWAY: (See *Clubs, Sewing.*) Let residents make two comforters, one for a girl and one for a boy. During the Christmas season, have kids, with their parents, come in and sign up for a chance to win them.

COMMUNITY MEETINGS: Offer your facility for community meetings— clubs, scouts, special groups. This builds good will, and when these groups are looking for a service project, you will probably be first in line.

DOLL HOUSE: (See *Projects.*)

DOLL SHOW: Have children of the community bring in their dolls. Have each child tell a little about her doll. Set up several categories (oldest, newest, most loved, tiniest, biggest) so every child wins a ribbon.

DOLLS FOR POOR CHILDREN: (See *Projects, Sock Dolls.*) These sock dolls can be made in number by residents and given to a community center or an orphanage. Children will love them.

EASTER EGGS, COLOR: Arrange for children to come to your facility and help residents color Easter eggs. This works well with a school class.

EASTER EGG HUNT: Hold an Easter egg hunt at your facility for kids of the community. Rent an Easter bunny costume, and let the bunny mingle with the kids while they hunt. Present a stuffed bunny to the one who finds the most eggs. See that no one goes home empty-handed.

GIFT-WRAPPING SERVICE: During the holiday season, offer a gift-wrapping service at your facility for the community. You probably would not want to charge, but you could accept donations, if offered, for your activity fund, or for any project for which you may be raising money. On the other hand, you may not want to accept donations, just offer it as a real service to the community. Solicit any resident who is capable of helping, to wrap and label. It would be good to put a volunteer in charge of this project so no errors are made.

LITTLE MISS CONTEST: Hold a beauty contest of sorts among little girls ages 5-7. Let them each model two or three outfits and perform, by singing, dancing or entertaining. Let residents act as judges. Give prizes. Serve simple refreshments.

MOVIE THEATRE: Set your activity room or dining room up as a movie theatre. Rent a 16mm Disney or other children's movie, and invite the public in to view it. Serve popcorn.

NURSING HOME OLYMPICS: (See *Monthly Biggies, Olympics.*)

PET SHOW: (See *Monthly Biggies.*)

PINEWOOD DERBY: (See *Projects.*)

PLANT SITTING AND HOSPITAL: If you have a light area to keep plants, offer a plant-sitting service to the community. People often need someone to care for their plants when they go on vacation or while they go to a warmer climate for the winter. Also, some just have unhealthy-looking plants that need some TLC. Perhaps your residents can nurse them back to health. Don't charge, but don't be surprised if donations are given. This helps buy plant care supplies. Residents enjoy repotting plants and caring for them.

QUILT SHOW: (See *Monthly Biggies.*)

REMINISCENT GROUP: Invite seniors from the community to visit your reminiscent group. Issue personal invitations to seniors you know, family members of residents or senior citizen's club members and church groups. (See *Any Day.*)

TOY REFINISHING: See *Projects*)

VACATION BIBLE SCHOOL: Hold a *Vacation Bible School* at your facility. Contact local churches who hold them for details on how to get started.

Chapter 14

Christmas

ADVENT CALENDAR: Buy an advent calendar. Each day, draw names to see which resident gets to open the little door over that particular day on the calendar and gets the chocolate treat under it. It is a good way to help residents keep track of how long it is until the big day.

ADVENT WREATH: If your facility believes in Christian doctrine, you might want to make an advent wreath which signifies the 4000 years waiting for the Messiah. The wreath is made from branches of greenery wrapped around a wire circle. Four candles are placed in it—three purple and one pink. One is lit each week of December.

AFTER CHRISTMAS: Ask children to come to your facility and show off their new toys. You will probably want to advertise it during Christmas week so parents and children will be prepared. Offer simple refreshments.

BAKE OR DECORATE COOKIES: Buy cookie dough or make your own and let residents cut out Christmas cookies and decorate them with sprinkles and colored sugar. Or you can buy sugar cookies and give residents icing to decorate them.

BELL CHOIR: If you don't know of a bell choir, check your larger churches. Residents enjoy hearing all the different sounds of the bells.

CALENDAR PLANNING: Beginning in November, let residents help plan the activity calendar for December. Let them decide what kind of cookies they would like to make, who they would like to have visit, and what type of parties they would like to have. As December gets underway you will not be able to follow their wishes exactly, but you can take them into consideration.

CANDY MAKING: (See *Cooking*.)

CAROLLERS: You seldom have to seek carollers out; they come to you. Don't turn away any if you can help it because this is good public relations for your facility. If they are welcomed kindly, they will remember your facility warmly and possibly provide you other activity throughout the year. You may have to schedule two or three groups on a given night, but that's okay. Try to schedule some groups on Saturdays and Sundays and chart these as weekend activities. This will make your job easier.

CHRISTMAS ANGEL VISIT: Santa always visits. On Christmas eve, why not start a tradition of having a little Christmas angel visit the residents. Before she leaves, let her put a statue of the Christ Child in the manger. This angel can be a child of a staff member who is comfortable visiting with residents.

CHRISTMAS PLAY: In about October or November, contact a nursery school teacher, and ask her if her children could provide a very simple play at your facility in December portraying the first Christmas. This is truly a heart-warming event for all who see it.

COMFORT GIVE-AWAY: (See *Clubs, Sewing,* and *Community.*)

DECORATION COLLECTING: Want to decorate your tree or your facility in a special way (all angels, bells, birds), but find yourself short of funds? People want to do kind things for health care facilities during the holiday season, so why not give them the opportunity? Send out requests to businesses, church groups, patrons and those who entertain at your facility, and ask for a decoration of your choosing. You will find yourself with a lovely collection at no cost to your facility. This could be an annual event. Since the request is so small, many will respond.

DOLL HOUSE: (See *Projects.*)

DOLLS: (See *Projects.*)

DOOR DECORATING CONTEST: Contact a school class (6th through high school), a woman's club or a sorority and ask them to be responsible for decorating residents' doors. Give a prize for the best one.

FILL-IN: Take a day just for fun. Have residents name Santa's reindeer. See who can recite *The Night Before Christmas.* Have them list all the Christmas songs they can, then play some and see who is the first one to guess the title. Ask them to tell about the best toys they ever received. Talk about toys of the past. Discuss how Christmas Day was spent long ago.

GIFT WRAPPING SERVICE: (See *Community.*)

PAPER CHAINS: (See *Crafts, Christmas.*)

PHOTO POST CARDS: During the late fall, many drug stores and photo places offer specials on postcards. Take photos of residents, and order them to be printed on postcards. Surprise residents' families with greetings from them.

PINE CONE DECORATIONS: Pine cones can be made into all kinds of decorations, and they are attractive. Just give residents glue, glitter, small beads, yarn and trinkets, and let them create colorful decorations.

SAINT NICK VISIT: On December 6th, the traditional feast of St. Nick, have him visit in his ancient costume (check library) along with his friend Rupert (a child). Rupert asks residents if they've been good or bad and suggests he will punish them if they've been bad. Have St. Nick pass out fruit and candy. In some countries, children set their shoes out for St. Nick to fill or they hang stockings. You could do this for residents, and let them find a special treat on the morning of December 6th.

SHOPPING 1: Many residents are unable to get out of the facility to shop, and other simply don't have access to money. Locate a church, women's club or sorority who want to adopt your facility every year or even for just for one year. The purpose is for the church or club to collect many gifts and bring them to your facility on a given day. When a group takes on this project, they sometimes work collecting items throughout the year.

At the time of resident shopping, the gifts are displayed on three tables, each table being coded with a color and featuring prizes of a specific value. For instance, the red table might have: knitted slippers, shawls, purses, wallets, dish towels and socks. The green table might feature items such as: shaving lotion, perfume, bath powder or knick knacks. The yellow table might display chewing gum, candy, and bookmarks.

Each resident is given three construction paper coupons that match the color on the tables. Then they are allowed to shop with the coupons as if they were money. In this way, residents feel they are shopping and paying for the items they receive. The host group can provide a gift-wrapping service, and the residents can then take the wrapped gifts to their room to give to their loved ones. (Don't be surprised if the residents want to shop for themselves and keep all the gifts. That's okay, too.)

SHOPPING 2: Invite several stores to set up shop in your activity room one day so residents can purchase items to give as gifts.

SIGNATURE TREE: Cut a large, flat Christmas tree from green poster board. Glue tiny sequins, decorations or miniature bows on the tip of each branch. Hang this in a prominent place, and have all guests and visitors sign it when they come to visit. Save it, and when you decorate next year, read the names of visitors to residents.

STRING POPCORN OR CRANBERRIES: Give residents threaded needles, and let them each string some popcorn. Attach all the finished strings together. (**Note:** It takes a lot of stringing to get enough. String berries in the same way. These are easier to string than popcorn because they are heavier and easier to hold on to.

TAFFY PULL: (See *Cooking.*)

TOY REFINISHING: (See *Projects.*)

TREE DECORATING: (See *Parties, Christmas Tree Trimming Party*)

Chapter 15

Parties

Everybody loves a party and residents are no different. Here are some you might want to try.

BACK TO SCHOOL PARTY: This is a good party to hold in August or September when school starts. For props, locate a large blackboard, and if possible, a couple school desks. Set up a table for teacher's desk. Rest a big dictionary and the Holy Bible on top because they were books used in residents' school days. Don't forget an apple for the teacher. A large picture of George Washington and Abraham Lincoln could be hung on the wall. From an appliance store, get a large refrigerator box, and decorate it to resemble an outhouse like the one where students once wore a path. Have a switch or a paddle hanging nearby and threaten to use it if any spit balls appear. Make a dunce cap and set a high stool in the corner.

Gather the students (residents) together and begin class. Have them recite their alphabet, and then put some addition and subtraction problems on the board. See if they can solve them. If so, move on to multiplication and finally long division. Have recess. There give the students marbles to play with as well as balls and jacks. After recess have a spelling bee and then review the states and capitals. Offer residents the capitals, and let them name the states.

Provide sandwich lunches in paper bags. After lunch, spend time reminiscing, letting residents recall what their classrooms looked like, what books they studied (ask about the McGuffey Reader, Webster's Elementary Speller and Kirkham's Grammar), and about any other memories from their school days.

As they leave for the day, you might turn tables a bit and give each of them an apple.

BACKWARDS PARTY: In order to get into the party, residents must each have something on backward, even if just a hat. Greet each resident who comes with "goodbye." When they leave say "hello." Ask them to recite their alphabet—backward—first as a group, then let individuals try. Read a traditional nursery

Parties
*
Family Events

Parties
*
Family Events

rhyme from the last line to the first. Have them count backwards from 100. Serve lunch starting with dessert and go to the appetizer.

BALLOON PARTY: Decorate with balloons of various sizes and shapes. Have a clown available to do tricks and to pass out balloons to residents. Locate a person who bends and ties long balloons together to make animals. Have a balloon launch as the grand finale.

CHRISTMAS PARTY: This is good held Christmas week, as near the holiday as possible. A sing-along with all the old carols puts residents in the Christmas spirit. You might read the scriptural account of the first Christmas from Matthew or Luke's Gospel. An interesting twist is to have Santa read it. Residents always enjoy a visit from the jolly old man in the red suit. Let him pass out presents to the residents. Serve cake or cookies and red punch.

CHRISTMAS TREE TRIMMING PARTY: Invite residents who are able, to help, and if some just want to watch, that's fine. Residents can hang decorations from their wheel chairs. Drape the lights, and then supervise residents as they decorate the tree. Serve hot chocolate when they are finished, and discuss how trees were decorated long ago (See Reference, *Remembering the Good Old Days, Christmas*.)

COOKOUT: Depending on where in the country you live, serve the appropriate food. Near the coast, it might include a clambake; elsewhere you could serve barbecued chicken, steaks or just hot dogs and hamburgers. Serve fresh corn on the cob and strawberry shortcake if in season. Have horseshoe available and lots of cold drinks.

FATHER'S DAY PARTY: Invite sons or son substitutes to have a father/son/grandson party. Cub scouts, boy scouts, Boy's Clubs, churches or men's organizations may be contacted to be substitute sons or grandsons. Make it an ugly tie affair. Have residents and guests wear the ugliest or most unique tie they can locate. Offer a prize for the ugliest. Ask each man to tell how many children he has. Ask how many remember the first time they became a father. Have them tell about it.

Ask if they ever changed diapers. Have a diaper changing contest pairing one resident with one guest. Use a doll, and if residents are incapable of fastening pins, a disposable diaper with stick tabs will do. Provide each man with a simple gift. (Thank goodness for bingo prizes). Serve cheese, crackers, pretzels and soda. Show a movie on auto racing or set up a bowling set and let them bowl.

FOURTH OF JULY PARTY: Help residents make colonial hats (See *Crafts*). Sing patriotic songs like *The Battle Hymn of the Republic* and *The Star Spangled Banner*. Talk about the Liberty Bell and Valley Forge. Tape names of famous people from history on each resident's back. Let residents give clues to each other until they have all guessed their famous person. These might include: Betsy Ross, Paul Revere, George Washington, Mark Twain and Franklin D. Roosevelt. If families are invited, this game may be easier. See if anyone remembers the poem about Paul Revere and the British coming. Discuss immigration, and ask from where residents or their ancestors immigrated. Try other pertinent word games. (See *Word Games*.)

HARVEST PARTY: Decorate with gourds, pumpkins and corn stalks. Bring in a variety of produce—apples, pumpkins, potatoes, beans, corn and wheat. Let residents examine it. Ask how many had gardens, and ask them to tell what they grew in them. Ask about ways of preserving food long ago (See Reference, *Remembering the Good Old Days*.) Serve cherry tomatoes and cucumber chunks. Slice up and serve to residents apples, pears and whatever fruit is prevalent in your area.

HOBO PARTY: Fashion a tripod, and from it hang a large pan supposedly to make "hobo stew." Cut out yellow and red construction paper flames and put under the pot. Ask residents to come in their oldest clothes. Give them paper patches to pin or tape on their clothes. When residents arrive, give each one a potato, turnip, ear of corn, green beans or something similar. Pass the pot around and let them each put in their vegetable to supposedly make hobo stew. (These are just props and not used.) Invite a fiddler in to play. Serve hobo stew (vegetable soup) from the kitchen in aluminum pie tins. Let residents discuss the days when hobos showed up at their doors. Ask if they fed them. Have them all sing *I've been Working on the Railroad*.

LAWN PARTY: In nice weather, gather residents outside for a lawn party like they had in the old days. Have a croquet game set up, and encourage residents to play. Serve ice cold lemonade and watermelon. Ask residents to notice the various kinds of birds flying, and then challenge them to name as many kinds as they can (See *Word Games*.)

MOTHER'S DAY TEA: Invite daughters, granddaughters and great-granddaughters. Locate substitutes daughters for those who don't have any. Try home economic clubs, churches or scouts groups. Let each mother introduce her family. Invite a craft shop worker in to give a craft or candy-making demonstration. Serve candies in fancy candy cups, and decorate with nice tablecloths, flowers and candles. Serve punch and cake or cookies.

PATRIOTIC PARTY: (See *Parties, 4th of July*.) This one could be held anytime, and families could be invited.

PIZZA PARTY: Though not quite the party as some, residents still enjoy a pizza party. Buy several, and let residents spend a pleasant afternoon or evening eating pizza and visiting with friends.

SHIP PARTY: Make your activity room resemble a ship's deck. Hang life savers (styrofoam wreaths) on the walls around the room. Use 2 by 4's stacked between bricks or blocks standing on end to make guard rails for the ship's edge. (Be sure not to place these blocks where residents could fall on them.) Make cardboard anchors, and have residents paint them. Hang large coiled ropes on the walls. Visit a travel bureau, and try to borrow some large posters about cruises. Hang signs about which say things like: *Swimming Off Port Side at 1:00, Watch Out for Sharks, Anchors Away* or *All Hands on Deck*.

Give each resident a passport. Sing *Anchors Away* and *Row, Row, Row Your Boat*. Dress as the captain, and get a uniform for the first mate. Try to find sailor hats for the residents. (Check party supply houses.) Serve lunch on deck, and then play shuffleboard. Check passports before anyone leaves the ship.

ST. PAT'S PARTY: Have residents make shamrocks from construction paper and decorate them with glue and glitter. Ask residents questions like "Who gets the credit for driving the snakes out of Ireland?" (Of course, St. Patrick.) Read a story about St. Patrick. Ask if anyone is Irish. Discuss things pertinent to the Irish. Talk about leprechauns and four-leaf clovers and blarney stones. Sing *When Irish Eyes Are Smiling* and *My Wild Irish Rose*.

THANKSGIVING: This is also a great occasion for a resident/family party (See *Family Events*). Help residents make little turkeys (See *Crafts*) for favors. Dig out your all-purpose tree (See *Crafts*), and set it up in a prominent place. Give each resident a scrap of paper as they come in and have them write on it one thing for which they are grateful. If they can't write, help them. Attach these to the blessing tree, and before everyone leaves, read their thanksgiving notes out loud. Serve a traditional Thanksgiving treat such as pumpkin pie with whipped cream.

VALENTINE PARTY: If residents haven't already made valentines in crafts, give them each several when they come in. Ask them to whom they would like to give a valentine. If they are unable to write or don't remember someone's name, they can just point, and you or a volunteer can write that name on the valentine. Let residents put their valentines in a big decorated valentine box (made earlier in crafts). Be sure there is a valentine already in the box for each resident so no one is left out. Have candy hearts in an attractive jar. Let residents guess how many are in the jar. The one who most nearly guesses the amount wins the candy jar (unless he or she is a diabetic). It pays to always have diabetic candy on hand.

Have someone play the piano and lead residents in some old love songs like *Let Me Call You Sweetheart*. Give everyone who can eat it, valentine candy hearts or red hots served in individual party cups. Serve valentine cake, cherry pie or just plain cherries and other fruits.

Chapter 16

Family Events

One of the best public relations tools available is to keep the families of residents happy and involved in your program. If they are happy with the care and activities your facility offers, they will be telling others it about it, and you'll be more apt to keep your beds full. Family parties are best held about four times a year. If more often, families can become overtaxed and bored with the involvement. If too seldom, some families may never get a chance to take part. Here's a few ways to involve families.

CAR SHOW: Ask a Model T car club to bring some automobiles for residents and their families to enjoy. In conjunction, you might plan a cook-out—frying hamburgers or roasting a pig—whatever your budget allows. Let residents look the cars over and reminisce. This is best held on a Saturday or Sunday afternoon in nice weather. A tractor show can be held in the same manner, and the men really enjoy it.

FASHION SHOW: (See *Monthly Biggies.*)

GAY NINETIES PARTY: Ask your local musuem if they'd either loan you a few outfits of the 1890's to display or send someone to model them. If so, hold a mini fashion show. Find a band that plays ragtime music. Collect items to display from the 1890's and early 1900's. These might include a shoe buttoner, old photos and frames, old kitchen utensils, a quilt and old tools. Check with a local antique store to see if they'd loan some items. Serve simple food like strawberry shortcake and whipped cream.

LUAU: You might decorate with fold-out paper Japanese lanterns hung from the ceiling. Buy or paint some huge palm trees, and secure Hawaiian posters from a travel agency to hang on the walls. Use candles on the tables and coconuts if you can find them. Let residents help make grass skirts from green trash bags by cutting slits in them. Either buy leis or let residents make them from funeral bouquet ribbons. Just sew long stitches up the center of each ribbon and then gather them. Several will need to be attached to make a lei. Locate someone who plays a ukelele or banjo for entertainment. Perhaps you can get Hawaiian dancers to do the Hula. Contact a local university to see if they have an international center that could supply the dancers. Play Hawaiian music while waiting for guests to arrive.

For refreshments, hollow out a watermelon by using a watermelon spoon to make tiny balls. Refill the shell with the watermelon balls, cantaloupe balls, green grapes, pineapple and strawberries. Have bananas on the table for decoration and for eating. Have bowls of coconut available for topping. With the fresh fruit, you might serve various cheeses and crackers. For beverage, offer a tropical fruit punch and coffee. Monday night has proven to be a fairly good night for family parties.

OKTOBERFEST: First, find your entertainment. Look for someone who plays German music. An accordion is great. Have them play some polkas. Maybe the entertainer will even wear the traditional German costume. A yodeler is nice, too. Decorate your room by covering the tables in red and white checked table covering. Put candles in bottles. Have bowls of pretzels on the tables for munching when guests enter. Plan to make this event a meal. Serve a German menu, perhaps bratwurst and sauerkraut or sauerbraten and dark rolls. You might add green beans and a black forest cake with whipped cream. Residents enjoy music so it's easy for them to get overtired. It's best to arrange beforehand to limit the entertainment to not more than an hour.

SHIP PARTY: (See *Parties.*) Invite families in for an evening of music on deck.

SQUARE DANCERS: Though this isn't exactly a party, invite families in to watch a square dance club perform. You might bring in a few bales of hay or straw for decoration and for the dancers to sit on. If you choose, serve supper before the dancing or simply supply refreshments mid-way through. This can be the climax for a Western Day. It can also be held in conjunction with a pie social.

THANKSGIVING SUPPER: Invite the residents' families to dinner at your facility early in Thanksgiving week. Have your kitchen prepare a turkey, dressing, vegetables, rolls and drinks. Ask each family to carry in a salad or dessert. After dinner, if you wish, provide some simple entertainment—a singer or a demonstration of residents' crafts. This might be a good time to hold a mini-bazaar to raise money for Christmas projects though the idea of family parties is to entertain them not to seek to gain from them. The meal will basically take most of the evening. Have all families who attend fill their resident's plate, and try to get the nursing staff to fill the plates of residents who are not ambulatory. This is always a successful activity.

Chapter 17

Clubs

Clubs serve a unique purpose. They can meet specific needs and address special interests in a small, non-threatening environment. Clubs encourage the forming of friendships as residents gather together to share common pursuits. Clubs do not have to be highly structured but they can be. Residents may want to wander in and out of various clubs until they find the ones they really enjoy. Here are a few you might want to try.

Beauty Club

No matter how old women become, they still enjoy looking nice. This is even true for confused ladies. Alert women can pretty much groom themselves, but for the confused female, this may be one of the few activities in which she participates. Hold the club weekly, or as time permits. You or a volunteer can gather a small group (The Raving Beauties Club???) around a table, and with a pail of warm water help them wash their face. Give them a comb or brush and let them brush their hair—as much as they are able. Then help them finish. Adding an attractive scarf might brighten some lady's spirits. Apply a touch of lipstick and finally dab on a little perfume. If you have extra time and want to do someone's nails, that is all the better. Prop a mirror on the table so they can see how nice they look.

Bowling Club

Those who once were bowlers will especially enjoy this one, but don't limit it just to them. Give your club a name. Arrange to take club members to a local bowling alley during off hours. You might set up your own bowling alley in your facility or outside on nice days. Use a ramp (See *Games, Bowling*) and let residents push

Clubs

*

Men Only

*

References and Resources

Clubs
*
Men Only
*
Reference

real bowling balls down it to knock down the pins on the floor beneath. See if you can get school kids to reset the pins. Watch bowling tournaments on T.V. Invite a bowler in to speak. Ask him or her to bring their trophies to share.

Cooking Club

Since women of yesteryear took great pride in their cooking, you may have many who want to join this club. Your club might try some of the recipes in the Cooking section. Here's some ideas to try.

BAKING: Depending on time, let them bake from prepared mixes or from scratch. Boxed muffins are quick and easy and good to eat. If time permits, help residents make bread, pies or cinnamon rolls. If making pies, they may choose to make crusts at one time and freeze them, and the next week prepare the fillings.

BREAK GREEN BEANS: When fresh green beans come on, let the cooking club sort and break the beans, and then cook them up in a crock pot with new potatoes and some bacon. They can have their own lunch.

FAIR: If residents are able, let them visit the county fair and check out the homemaking area where home-baked goodies and canned foods are displayed. If unable, bring in sample produce and let residents inspect it.

NOODLES: Let your residents make noodles, each one their own batch. Mix them together and let the noodles dry a bit. Meanwhile, help them put a chicken on to cook in a slow cooker. You may need two cookers. During the last hour or so, they can add their noodles. Let them each invite a family member to share their meal.

RESTAURANT: Residents might want to tour different restaurants in your area. Fast food restaurants often arrange tours of the facility. Another idea is to *eat* at various restaurants. They do not have to be expensive ones. Sometimes the quaint little out-of-the-way places are the best.

Couples Club

You might want to form a club for married couples in your facility. Often this group is not large.

BOAT RIDE: If there's a river boat within 30 or 40 miles of your facility and residents are able to be transported, by all means, take them on a cruise down the river. Usually lunch or snacks are served on the boat.

COMPANY: Work with other activity directors and facilities in your area to get your couples clubs together for events. This could include card-playing, a picnic, a croquet game or lunch.

ICE CREAM SOCIALS: Let couples meet together and visit over ice cream sundaes, root beer floats and banana splits.

MEALS: Provide special meals for them monthly, apart from the other residents. This can be in a separate room or at a different time. Make these dinners as pleasant as possible by using a table cloth, candles, nice glassware and cloth napkins. Encourage conversation so the couples become acquainted. Look for common interests in order to plan special activities for them.

PARK OUTING: If couples are able, take them to the park. If they are not able to get out and walk, just drive through the park. You may want to stop the van, and let them enjoy watching the children and young lovers.

ROMANTIC MOVIES: Let couples enjoy some of the old movies where there was real romance but little sex on the screen. Serve popcorn.

SPOON BY THE LIGHT OF THE MOON: On nice, warm starry evenings, arrange lawn chairs outside and encourage couples to just enjoy being together.

History Club

This can be a really fun club since so very much history has taken place during residents' lives. They are a unique generation among all those from the beginning of history. They have seen more drastic changes in the world than any other people before them. Draw on that knowledge during your history club. *Remembering the Good Old Days* (See Reference) is a helpful tool for the 1890 through 1945 era because it offers 100 old-days subjects broken down into a series of questions about those days. You might pick a different subject and discuss it each time you meet.

Meet once a month or more often if desired. At the first meeting, talk about history and see where interests lie · Go to the library and locate books and visual aids concerning the eras residents are most interested in. Some areas might be:

AMERICA BECOMING A NATION: Read up on and share about the Revolutionary War. Locate pictures of uniforms. Spend a session talking about George Washington as a boy, husband, Christian, surveyor, soldier and president. Discuss Paul Revere. Read the famous poem about the British coming. Talk about the Boston Tea Party, and try to locate picture drawings of it.

AMERICAN INDIANS: Show movies on the American Indians. Discuss their being forced onto reservations. Ask if residents knew any Indians personally. Read stories about Indians. See if your museum has any Indian artifacts that they might bring to your facility. Ask an Indian buff to speak to your history club. Take residents to an outdoor Indian drama re-enactment if there is one in your area.

AVIATION: Discuss with residents the first time they saw an airplane. Show pictures and possibly a model of the Wright Brothers' plane. Discuss the Lindbergh flight. Let them talk about Amelia Earhart. Read to them about Wiley Post, the one-eyed pilot and all that he accomplished. Locate books about these flyers and share them together.

CIVIL WAR ERA: Locate information on various battles and discuss it with residents. Buy toy soldiers as visual aids. Invite a Civil War buff to talk to residents. Check out your local art museum for paintings; see if they will bring them in for residents to enjoy. Ask your county museum to bring actual Civil War uniforms and other articles from that era for residents to view. Show movies on the Civil War. Check out old maps. Ask residents if they had any family members in that war. Discuss.

ENTERTAINERS OF THE PAST: Will Rogers is always a good entertainer to discuss. Residents loved him. At the library you can find books containing his famous sayings like, "I never met a man I didn't like." Let the residents share what they remember about this man—how great a humanitarian he really was.

Movie stars such as Mary Pickford, America's sweetheart of the silent movies, Clara Bow, the "it" girl, Clark Gable and Rudolph Valentino were favorites. Locate pictures of them. Show movies in which some of the old favorites starred.

Discuss vaudeville and some of its performers. Ask about Kate Smith. Play one of her records for residents. Research Tom Mix, the famous cowboy who was supposedly wounded numerous times in his movies. Have someone bring in a very old radio and let residents discuss the early radio programs. Also discuss some of the early sponsors. Show a Marx Brothers' film.

SETTLING OF THE WEST: Find diaries (check the library) of women who traveled via wagon train to the west. Discuss the hardships they had. Show some old *Wagon Train* shows. Display a mock-up of a conestoga wagon, and discuss how it withstood the trip and how it was packed with supplies and what they might have been.

THIRTIES: Interview residents who lived through the tough times about how they survived. Find price lists from those days. Check your library for old Sears catalogs put out in the 30's. Look for art work done under government projects like the WPA. Discuss Franklin D. Roosevelt and his policies. Research them at the library.

Through your library, find which songs and movies were popular. Invite a musician in who will play some of the thirties songs. Check out fashions of that era.

In Addition You Might Try These

ANTIQUE STORE VISIT: Visiting an antique store is like a trip back in history. Old country stores, made to resemble the stores in our residents' day, make an interesting outing.

HOME TOUR: If residents are able, visit a few old homes in the area. Your museum may help you make arrangements.

LIBRARY VISIT: Take able residents to the library, and let them uncover some of history's treasures.

MUSEUM VISIT: For those who can get out, the museum can offer a wonderful trip through history.

Horticulture Club

This club could meet once a month. If you can locate a volunteer to lead it, so much the better. If you have a university nearby, it's possible you can get a volunteer club leader from there. If not, a garden club or just an individual with a green thumb might undertake the project. Here's a few things you might try.

BEDSIDE PLANT CARE: Bed patients and some other residents are unable to care for their own plants. The horticulture club could be semi-responsible to care for these.

BOTTLE GARDEN: For each garden, you will need a large wide-mouth bottle and a tuna can. Gather plants from plant lovers, a nursery, or better yet, go into a woods and gather wild mosses, ferns and plants along with a little of their natural soil. Poke holes with a nail in the bottom of the tuna can, and then add a few small rocks or broken pieces of a clay flower pot. Next, add either the potting soil or soil you collected in the woods. Moisten it and plant your greenery.

Place the large mouth bottle over your plants and carefully slip the jar lid under the tuna can and screw it on.

Growing plants in a bottle creates high humidity so they can grow away from their natural homes. In bottle gardens or terrariums, plants are enclosed and do not require much water **because** moisture can't escape. They will let you know when they need water by showing signs of wilting. Give adequate light. When the plants have grown too large, trim them back a little.

GROW FRUIT TREES: Save seeds from peaches, oranges, apples and other fruits. Put these in the deep freeze for a few weeks. (This makes the seed think it has gone through a winter.) Now, have residents plant the seeds in flower pots. Label them carefully and chart their growth.

GRASS GARDEN: Locate long potatoes like *Idaho's*, and have residents scoop out most of the inside but leave about 1/4 inch of potato inside the peel. It will resemble a canoe. Have them fill this with potting soil and then sprinkle this with grass seed. Let them gently water it. In a couple weeks, they will have an inside lawn.

INDOOR GARDEN: Have residents fill bedding trays with soil, and let them plant tomatoes and peppers seeds and watch them grow. When they're big enough, transfer them to buckets and finally outside when weather permits.

PLANT CARE: Spread newspaper all over an activity room table, and let residents pull the dead leaves off the plants and repot them.

ROOT SWEET POTATO: Select potatoes with some buds at one end. Fill glasses or jars, slightly larger than the potato, mostly full of water. Stick tooth picks in each side of the potato so they will hold the potato half-in and half-out of the glass of water. Put the buds at the top, and immerse the bottom half of the potato in the water. Keep the potato in the light, but avoid a place where the sun might get to it. Add water as needed. Before long, roots will sprout. Wait another month or so, and then transfer it to a flowerpot large enough for the roots to spread out in the soil. Soon you'll have a lovely plant.

SALT GARDEN: It's fun for residents to watch the changes as the salt grows. You'll need salt, water, vinegar and a few pieces of coal. (Some porous stones will do if coal is unavailable. Porous stones are lighter than other stones and seem to be literally full of small holes.) Fill a bowl about half full of warm water and begin adding salt, a spoon at a time, until it is completely dissolved. Keep adding more salt until no more will dissolve in the water. Add a tablespoon of vinegar to the mixture and stir. Now completely fill the bowl of salty water with the coal or stones. Set it aside, and in a day or so, salt crystals will start to grow on top of the coal. Let the salt crystals grow for several days. The water in the bowl will evaporate. At that point, you can remove the crystals stones or leave them in the salt garden.

Hospitality Club

SERVE REFRESHMENTS: The hospitality club may want to help you serve refreshments at activities, or may deliver them to residents off a cart in the hall.

VISIT SICK: When a resident is bedfast or not feeling well, club members can visit that resident.

WELCOME GUESTS: When you are unable to welcome guests who come to your facility to entertain residents, put this committee in charge.

WELCOME NEW RESIDENTS: Let club members decide how best to welcome new residents. They may pay a personal visit the first day and give a card, flowers, candy (if appropriate) or a small gift.

Literary Club

Innumerable people have the desire to write. Others like to read good writers' works. Here's where a literary club comes in. Check with interested residents to find what they want out of a club. Here's some suggestions.

BOOK READING: Have a volunteer or a resident with a clear voice read an interesting book to the club members—a chapter a week or so. It's important not to read too long and to break regularly to discuss what's being read. Books written about the time when residents were young are interesting. Also, books about famous people they remember such as Will Rogers or Franklin Roosevelt. You might want to read about Tom Sawyer and Huckleberry Finn and from other classics.

If residents are able to read themselves, gather them in a comfortable place for reading time. When someone completes a book, ask if they will give a short oral report about it.

DIARIES AND JOURNALS: Give each resident who will participate a small notebook or diary, and let them record their daily thoughts and happenings.

LIBRARY VISIT: If residents are able, take them to the library. Have a tour arranged, if possible, so the librarian can show them around. Let them spend time sitting at a table looking at a book that interests them. Another visit might show them how to locate information in a library. Make this a regular outing.

If residents are unable to go to the library, there's a good chance a library employee will come to them. She can bring good books and discuss them. She may want to read to them.

PUBLISHING FIRM VISIT: Perhaps you have a book bindery or publishing firm in your area. Maybe its just a small publisher. See if your residents can view the process in action.

SPEAKERS: Locate some local writers, and one at a time, invite them in to speak to your group. The writing field is so broad that you should probably give them a topic you want them to address. This may include: the working life of a writer; how to get started in writing; how you might improve your writing; the process a book goes through before it is finally sold. They might also speak on different kinds of writing: greeting cards, short stories, articles or novels.

WRITE: Set aside some gatherings just to write. Give members a topic, and ask them to write about the home of their childhood or what they remember about the Great Depression or the first time they saw an automobile or an airplane. If they are unable to write, perhaps a volunteer will record their thoughts. At other times, let them write a poem or just let free verse flow from them. It's important, to many writers, to be published. Give them the opportunity. Print their work and byline in your newsletter (with their permission, of course).

Men's Club

Whenever possible, get the men away from the facility for an activity. In a mostly female environment, it's vital that men have time aside from joint activities to spend with other males. Belonging to the Men's Club offers them this opportunity. It's encouraging to see more men coming into the field of activities. They can, no doubt, meet some needs that are difficult for us female activity directors to meet.

The club can meet once a week, or once a month, or just when there's a men's activity planned. (See *Men Only* .) All the activities there can be used in the club. In addition, you might even want to try a little cooking. Find out what they would like to eat, and if some of them want to try their hand, let them cook a simple recipe or even a whole meal. Here's a few more ideas for you to pursue for the men's club.

AIRPORT VISIT: Contact a small to medium size airport, and try to arrange for your men to view an airplane up close and to get inside. Perhaps you can even arrange a short flight for them. First, of course, get a signed permission slip from families.

AUTOMOBILES: Take them to a car museum, and let them reminisce over those goodies of the past. Supply them with historic auto books and magazines, and let them browse through them and discuss the great old cars.

Locate a race car driver to speak to your men. Hold an antique auto show at your facility. Arrange for someone to give rides to your men in antique cars.

Show movies about cars and car races. If you know a mechanic who enjoys the elderly, ask him to bring a car to your facility one afternoon and let residents who are mechanically inclined putter with the engine. Take men to a new car show held at the fairgrounds or elsewhere, or just take them to a new car lot and let them look over the cars. If they are able, take your men to a stock car race. You probably would not be able to stay for entire evening, but they'd enjoy it for a while.

FARM VISIT: (See *Outings*.)

HORSES: Invite someone to bring a few horses to your facility for the men to groom and enjoy. Perhaps they could even go for a ride in a cart pulled by a horses. Be sure to secure permission from their families first. Take them to a horse show.

Sewing Club

Most facilities have a few ladies who really like to sew. With this in mind, gather them together and encourage them to select a name for their club. Perhaps *The Thimbles* or *The Fine Seam Club*. Decide how often to meet and what residents would like to do.

Ask a Home Demonstrations club to come and discuss the sewing aspects of homemaking. Invite a fabric store employee to talk on modern fabrics or sewing techniques or new products not available in residents' prime sewing years. Invite a high school home economics teacher in to speak on sewing.

Spend time looking at needlework books together. Begin a button collection, and ask each resident to donate some of their buttons. Invite guests in to speak on crochet, embroidery, knitting, tatting, rug braiding and other needlework. Work on community projects like sewing for the needy or making baby gowns for hospital nurseries. Here's a few other ideas you might try.

DOLL MAKING: (See *Projects, Doll Making*.)

FAIR: Let any residents who are able, visit the county fair and check out the clothing area. Let them examine the quilts and the clothing, and see if it passes residents' inspection for fine seams.

If residents are unable to go to the fair, contact the 4-H center and see if you can locate 4-H members who will bring their sewing projects to the facility for residents to view.

FREE SEW: Let everyone bring their own particular project and join in a comfortable area to work on it. This may be knitting, embroidery, crochet or mending. Free Sew can be used regularly when nothing special is planned (like weekends). It's just a chance for ladies of similar interest to get together and visit while their hands are busy doing something they love.

LAP ROBES: The sewing club may want to make lap robes for the facility. Provide them with fabric, and let them cut out 6-inch blocks and sew them together. Next give them some soft material for the back and let them knot the quilt top and the backing together. Help them sew around the edges.

MENDING: The sewing club may want to help with the facility mending, or at least that of residents who do not have family members to do it. Here's a chance for the club to bring in a little money that they can use to purchase supplies. Staff members never seem to have time to do their mending, so they may be willing to pay the sewing club to do simple sewing tasks for them.

TEDDY BEARS: These are really easy to make. On newspaper, lay down a large teddy bear and draw around its shape with marker. This is your pattern. Purchase brown terry cloth and just a little white terry cloth. Fold the fabric in half and pin the pattern to the brown terry. Cut out both pieces at once. On the wrong side, sew around the whole bear leaving a few inches between the legs for turning. Stuff.

Now, cut a circle of white terry cloth about 6-inches around (depending on the size of your bear). This will be the face and nose area. Sew it by hand to the center of the bear's face leaving a couple inches free to stuff it real fat. Sew the opening shut. In the center of that, attach a small black felt circle for the nose. Cut and attach small black felt circles for the eyes and white terry circles for the inside of the ears. Tie a colorful ribbon around its neck. These will usually sell well among staff and visitors to the facility, especially if made in November or December.

QUILT COMFORTERS: (See *Any Day*.)

Traveling Club

For residents who like to travel but are no longer able, here's a way to still enjoy their hobby. Invite people in who travel and let them share about their trips to various places and show their slides or movies. Invite a travel agent to talk on travel. Ask him to bring some large travel posters to display. Gather residents around a table, and let them peer over *National Geographic* and travel magazines. They can tell about trips they would like to take if they could. Ask an airline flight attendant or commercial pilot to share about their jobs and the places they visit. Arrange short trips on a train or plane or bus or boat. Have lunch and return to the facility.

Chapter 18

Men Only

Since activity directors are most often female, and consequently think as females, they often find it hard to come up with activities for men. Here are a few that have proven successful with men in some facilities.

BASEBALL GAME: If residents are able, take them to a youth baseball game in a park where there's easy access. You can leave whenever they get tired. At some ball fields, you can drive right up near the field so residents can watch without having to leave the van.

BASKETBALL GAME: Invite the coach and some team members from a local college or high school in to play a game of nursing home basketball with your men (See *Games* for rules). Serve refreshments afterwards.

You could also take your residents to a high school basketball game. Arrange for seating beforehand. You might want to ask for folding chairs to be set up in front of the bottom bleacher. Don't overlook going to grade school basketball games. Another option is to arrange with a coach to let you watch them practice.

BIBLE STUDY: Women generally carry the load of spiritual activities, but men may well enjoy having an all male Bible study. Contact local churches for male volunteers to lead the group.

BOWLING: Arrange with a bowling alley to bring your men to bowl. If you go in the morning, perhaps you could take your men out to lunch and then for a stroll or a ride around the park.

CAMPING TRIP: (See *Monthly Biggies*.)

CAR DEALERSHIP: Men love automobiles. There's been many changes since those early cars which residents started out driving. Why not take a group of men to a car dealership, and let them look over the new cars—and the prices! If the men are unable to leave the facility, arrange for a dealer to bring two or three new cars to your facility for residents to view.

CHECKER AND CHESS TOURNAMENTS: (See *Games.*)

FAIR: (See *Outings.*)

FOOTBALL GAMES: (Same as for basketball.) There are also electronic football games that may prove fun for some.

GARDENING: Many men were farmers. If your facility has a garden, and any of your men are able to help—even hoe from a wheelchair— encourage them to do it. Short of that, they might help keep weeds pulled from outside flower beds. They may enjoy planting and tending an inside garden in window boxes.

HANDYMEN: Many male residents were once handymen who liked to tinker with small appliance repair. Go to garage sales or ask friends and staff for non-working appliances such as toasters, older-style radios, irons, mixers and sweepers. Older items are more mechanical and simpler to fix. The men may enjoy locating the problems and might possibly even fix the appliances. Even confused men (with supervision) can be given a small non-heating appliance and a screwdriver; they may enjoy the diversion. With any of these, you will need to supervise so no harm comes to anyone.

HORSE RACING: There's a boxed horse racing game called Casino Downs on the market where small plastic horses march down a six-foot green vinyl track. Their moves are determined by a roll of a dice. It can be purchased from *Medical and Activity Sales* (See Reference.) Gather the men together for a night (or afternoon) at the races.

HORSESHOE: Take your men to the park, and let them pitch horseshoes. For those still at the facility, arrange for them to play inside with rubber horseshoes.

KENTUCKY DERBY OR INDIANAPOLIS 500 RACE: Watch your T.V. listings for broadcasts of such events. Notify the men and plan to make it a "men's activity." Take the ladies elsewhere. Serve the men lunch or just pretzels and soda in front of the television.

MEN'S BREAKFAST: Solicit some volunteers, then bring out the griddles and cook up something just for the men. This might be pancakes or french toast, eggs and bacon, grits or fried mush. You might want to order fresh rolls from a local bakery. Have plenty of coffee available. You may even want to show a morning movie that men would enjoy. Check your local library. Offer them the newspaper to read when breakfast is finished.

MEN'S LUNCHEON: Once a month, in a smaller room away from the usual dining area, schedule a special luncheon just for the men. Invite a guest speaker to each lunch. Guest speakers might include: a football or basketball coach, a minister, well-known athlete, politician, fireman, teacher or race car driver. You might also consider a carpenter, farmer, recruiter, newspaperman, restaurant owner, or a television or radio personality. Have them just share a little about their jobs and their lives. You might invite speakers with similar jobs to those your residents once held. Perhaps they can bring visual aids along. Talks should be no longer than 20 to 30 minutes.

MONDAY NIGHT AT THE FIGHTS: This can be done in several ways. Contact your local high school wrestling team, and invite some wrestlers to bring their mats and come wrestle in the middle of your activity or dining room. When the team leaves, you might serve your men light beer and pretzels (if their diets allow.)

Another easier way is to gather the men together and turn the T.V. to wrestling. They may want to guess ahead of time who will win. Give prizes to the winner. Serve light beer or soda, and cheese and crackers, as diets permit.

You could also take your residents to an actual fight. Sometimes these are held at the local armory.

TRADE MAGAZINES: Collect trade magazines put out for the readership of a variety of occupations. Some might be *Ford Times* put out by the Ford Motor Company and airline magazines like *U.S Air*. Others have to do with the building trade, grocery trade, fishing, medical, farming, selling and so on. If you get a big enough variety, there will be something for every one. Gather the men together, and let them browse through the magazines. With a little encouragement, they'll probably soon become involved in discussions of their previous occupations and other jobs they've held in their lifetime.

Other Books by the Author
(prices subject to change)

Sailing To Your Success: **"Keys to Your Personal and Professional Development"** Shows you how to reach your full potential in life and on the job and covers such subjects as: being freely yourself and loving it, growing into who you really are, recognizing and developing your unique gifts, leadership struggles and solutions, polishing your people-pleasing powers, and how attitude begins with you. It also discusses, goal-setting, time management, coping constructively with criticism, and solutions to clutter, confusion, and chaos. But that's not all. You'll find professional pointers, uncover the benefits of "giving" freely, recognize friendship as a gift you give yourself, and discover that failure is really a stepping stone on the way to your success. This book will make you proud to be active in your current profession and happy to be the unique person you really are! **$16.99.**

How to Thrive Not Just Survive in Life and in the Activity Profession
Many books are written about residents' needs, but this one is not for them but for you, the activity professional. Designed to help you thrive in activities, it covers ways to organize your life, make your office more manageable, to run your department on a shoestring budget, to make the phone work *for* you not against you, and how to let your excellence exceed your employer's expectations. In addition, it shows you how to handle stressful situations, to get the most out of activity conferences, and to let your activities shine out in the community. It further discusses how residents' well-being begins with your own, how to look and feel your best, how to dress in a professional manner, and how to be safe when you travel. Perfect-bound, 160 pages, **$16.99.**

Mystery Person of the Week: Who Am I? 52 Weeks of Bulletin Board Fun
Need something to keep residents busy on weekends while you are not there? Here is a fun and mentally challenging activity. Hang a set of our clues on your bulletin board before you leave on Friday, and let residents guess who the mystery person is. If necessary, add more clues on Monday, and even more on Wednesday, and continue adding until they guess. Give a prize to the winner. All personalities are ones residents would know: Presidents and their wives, Will Rogers, John Dillinger, Shirley Temple, Lucy, etc. Fifty-two mystery persons are provided with many, many clues for each. Just copy a page of clues and hang them up. Instant activity! **$22.99** (available 2004)

Activities Encyclopedia: **"535 Best Activity Ideas"**
Many of these great activity ideas were contributed by activity professionals across the nation and Canada. Activities are divided into 13 categories: parties, men-only, cooking, special projects, crafts, guests, outings, games/word games, bedside and low-functioning, community outreaches, monthly biggies, and everyday activities. This user-friendly book features reinforced tabs and alphabetized listings of activities to help you locate any activity quickly. It is also indexed. 191 pages, conveniently wiro-bound, 191 pages, **$33.99.**

-more-

Activity Planning at Your Fingertips: **"All the Activities You'll Ever Need"** *Activity Planning at Your Fingertips* is a user-friendly guide created especially for the busy activity professional. There are over 600 great activities, and two years of pre-planned activity calendars that you are free to copy and use. The book is divided into ten tabbed sections. Each section's activities are then alphabetized to help you locate any activity quickly. There are activity ideas for bedside, low-functioning, holiday parties, family parties, cooking, crafts, exercise, games, fill-ins, Christmas, men-only, outings, clubs, community outreaches, special projects, monthly biggies, and everyday activities. 208 pages, wirobound, **$33.99.**

The Professional Activity Director: **"Be All You Want to Be"**
In a lively, upbeat conversational style, the author tackles such subjects as recognizing and developing your professional image, getting along with staff, dressing professionally, getting press coverage, community involvement, beating burnout, running a volunteer program, and dealing with problems common to activity directors. There are also many activity ideas, valuable resources, word games and medical terms. 174 pages, **$16.99.**

Newsletters Simplified: **"Valuable Information to Print in Your Newsletter, Plus Helpful Newsletter Tips"**
If you like trivia, you'll love this book. It's definitely NOT just for those who do newsletters. There are 352 pages packed full of arresting information to put in your newsletter **OR** to use for activities. There are reminiscent articles by Marge Knoth to copy and use. There's exciting data about Lindbergh, Earhart, Dillinger, Roosevelt, Will Rogers, Shirley Temple, and more. In addition, you'll find facts about the 1920's, 30's, 40's, World War I and II, and the Great Depression. You'll also find presidential trivia, holiday trivia, quotable quotes, old-time prices, one-liners, comforting scriptures, and funny stories told by nursing home residents. In addition to 12 chapters of informative and fun trivia, there are another five "how-to" chapters to help you put together a great newsletter. **$22.99**

Remembering the Good Old Days: **"Lively Reminiscent Group Starters"**
All you need to lead a lively reminiscence group with no prior planning. Offers 100 old-time subjects, each broken down into thoughtful questions (which lead to the answers) which quickly draw the elderly into discussion. Some subjects are: old-time beauty secrets, barn dances, immigration, dance marathons, famous people, preserving food, weddings, and childbirth. There are 21 tips for leading a lively reminiscence group, photos and illustrations, old-time prices, and 19th-century helpful hints. Perfect- bound, 130 pages, **$14.99.**

Looking Back: **"Reminiscent Party Fun for Senior Citizens--200 Questions and Answers"**
Looking Back is small but packed full of reminisence activity. It offers 200 challenging questions and answers about life long ago. Also many one-liner "Do You Remember?" discussion starters. Great for any time you need a quick activity or want to stimulate the elderly to reminisce. Lots of photos and illustrations. Perfect-bound, 85 pages, **$12.99.**

Most Recent
Books by the Author

Mystery Person of the Week: Who Am I?
Mystery Person provides you with a unique bulletin board or group activity for all 52 weeks of the year. Each of the mystery persons are divided into six to nine days worth of clues, clues that become progressively easier with each passing day. Without you even being present, this book continues to provide fun activity for residents, staff, and visitors. The mystery persons are all well-known personalities whom your residents or students should know–Frank Sinatra, Benjamin Franklin, Mother Theresa, Oprah Winfrey, Annie Oakley. Clues are printed in large print so you have only to copy the day's clues and tack them on the board. The next day tape that days clues to the first. And so on till the mystery person is guessed. *Or...*use the book as a group activity, throwing out clues for residents to guess. Great party entertainment too! **$32.99**

Tips, Tricks, and Tempting Ideas for Activity Professionals
It's always fun to share ideas with other activity professionals. This book gives you the feeling of having a colleague right there with you, sharing ideas faster than you can write them down. Here you'll find 212 tips, tricks and activity ideas that the author has learned in her nearly 30 years in the activity field. Ideas are shared for big and small events, resident council, group activities, clubs, fund-raising, motivation, personal growth, and more. Like the author's books, *Activity Planning at Your Fingertips* and *Activities Encyclopedia*, this book, too, is designed with the busy activity professional in mind. It is divided according to subject and is then broken up into short, readable and numbered paragraphs. If you are in need of some fresh ideas and some encouragement, this one is for you. **$24.99**.

For the Busy Activity Professional

Two Full Years
of

Pre-Planned Activity Calendars

January

Sunday	Monday	Tuesday	Wednesday	Thursday	Friday	Saturday
	1 NEW YEAR! MONDAY	**2** 10:00 Do You Remember? / 11:45 States & Capitals / 2:00 Cooking Club (Fruit Salad) / 6:00 Social Hour	**3** 9:00 Bedside Act (9-11) / 11:30 Exercise / 11:45 Devotions / 2:00 Bingo	**4** 9:00 Beauty Club (9-11) / 11:30 20 Questions / 2:00 Newsletter / 3:00 Catholic Mass / 7:00 Social Hour	**5** 10:00 Tape Listening / 11:30 Exercise / 11:45 Devotions / 3:00 History Club	**6** 9:00 Coffee Group / 2:00 Old Radio / 6:00 Checkers & Scrabble
7 9:00 Coffee Group / 2:00 Church / Family Visits	**8** 9:00 Bedside Act (9-11) / 11:30 Exercise / 2:00 Bible Study / 3:00 Sewing Club (Free Sew)	**9** 10:00 Do You Remember? / 11:30 Name That Tune / 11:45 Devotions / 2:00 Craft Club	**10** 9:00 Bedside Act (9-11) / 11:30 Exercise / 11:45 Devotions / 2:00 Bingo / 6:00 Band	**11** 9:00 Beauty Club (9-11) / 11:30 Jokes & Riddles / 2:00 Men's Club (Coach Speaking) / 3:00 Catholic Mass	**12** 9:00 Music Appreciation (9-11) / 11:30 Exercise / 2:00 Outing Pizza Parlor	**13** 9:00 Coffee Group / 2:00 Plant Care / 6:00 Movie
14 9:00 Coffee Group / 2:00 Church / 3:00 Scrabble	**15** 9:00 Bedside Act (9-11) / 11:30 Exercise / 2:00 Horticulture Club (Plant Care)	**16** 10:00 Do You Remember? / 11:30 States & Capitals / 2:00 Cooking Club (Biscuits) / 6:00 Social Hour	**17** 9:00 Bedside Act (9-11) / 11:30 Exercise / 11:45 Devotions / 6:00 Evening Movie	**18** 9:00 Beauty Club (9-11) / 11:30 Word Games / 2:00 Wild Game Hunt / 3:00 Catholic Mass	**19** 10:00 Reading Group / 11:45 Similies / 2:00 Basketball Game	**20** 9:00 Coffee Group / 2:00 Bird Feeding & Watching / 6:00 Movie
21 9:00 Coffee Group / 2:00 Church / 6:00 Old Radio	**22** 9:00 Bedside Act (9-11) / 11:30 Exercise / 2:00 Bible Study / 3:00 Hospitality Club	**23** 10:00 Do You Remember? / 11:30 Math Quiz / 2:00 Resident Council / 6:00 Social Hour	**24** 9:00 Bedside Act (9-11) / 11:30 Exercise / 11:45 Devotions / 2:00 Bingo	**25** 9:00 Beauty Club (9-11) / 2:00 Old Proverbs / 3:00 Catholic Mass	**26** 11:30 Exercise / 2:00 Baby Loving Day / 6:00 Guitar Player	**27** 9:00 Coffee Group / 2:00 Old Radio / 8:00 Wheel of Fortune
28 9:00 Coffee Group / 2:00 Church / 6:00 Movie	**29** 9:00 Bedside Act (9-11) / 11:30 Exercise / 11:45 Devotions / 2:00 Literary Club	**30** 10:00 Do You Remember? / 11:30 Similies / 2:00 Men's Club / 6:00 Wine & Cheese	**31** 9:00 Bedside Act / 11:30 Exercise / 11:45 Devotions / 2:00 Literary Club			

February

Valentine's Day!

Sunday	Monday	Tuesday	Wednesday	Thursday	Friday	Saturday
				1 9:00 Beauty Club (9-11) 11:30 Old Proverbs 11:45 Patriotic Quiz 3:00 Catholic Mass	**2** 9:00 Coffee & Newspaper 11:30 Exercise 11:45 Devotions 2:00 Rhythm Band	**3** 9:00 Coffee Group 2:00 Plant Care 6:00 Movie
4 9:00 Coffee Group 2:00 Church 3:00 Scrabble	**5** 9:00 Bedside Act. (9-11) 11:30 Exercise 2:00 Birthday Party	**6** 10:00 Do You Remember? 11:45 Devotions 12:00 Winter Picnic & Games (12-2)	**7** 9:00 Bedside Act. (9-11) 11:30 Exercise 11:45 Devotions 2:00 Bingo	**8** 9:00 Beauty Club (9-11) 11:30 Song Titles 2:00 History Club (Depression) 3:00 Catholic Mass 7:00 Social Hour	**9** 9:00 Bedside Act. (9-11) 11:30 Exercise 11:45 Devotions 2:00 Bingo 6:00 Band	**10** 9:00 Coffee Group 2:00 Old Radio 6:00 Checkers & Scrabble
11 2:00 Coffee Group Family Visits	**12** 9:00 Bedside Act (9-11) 11:30 Exercise 2:00 Bible study 3:00 Sewing Club (Valentine Pin Cushions)	**13** 10:00 Do You Remember? 11:30 Bird Quiz 2:00 Cooking Club (Cherry Delight) 6:00 Social Hour	**14** 10:00 Tape Listening 11:30 Exercise 11:45 Devotions 2:00 Valentine Party	**15** 9:00 Beauty Club (9-11) 11:30 Jokes & Riddles 2:00 Men's Club (Euchre) 3:00 Catholic Mass	**16** 9:00 Music Appreciation (9-11) 11:30 Exercise 1:00 Outing Library	**17** 9:00 Coffee Group 2:00 Plant Care 6:00 Movie
18 9:00 Coffee Group 2:00 Church 6:00 Old Radio	**19** 9:00 Bedside Act. (9-11) 11:30 Exercise 2:00 Horticulture Club (Plant Care)	**20** 10:00 Do You Remember? 11:30 States & Capitals 2:00 Resident Council 6:00 Social Hour	**21** 9:00 Bedside Act. (9-11) 11:30 Exercise 11:45 Devotions 2:00 Bingo 7:00 Barber Shop Quartet	**22** 9:00 Beauty Club (9-11) 11:30 Word Games 2:00 Soap Bubble Fun 3:00 Catholic Mass	**23** 10:00 Reading Group 11:30 Exercise 2:00 Basketball Game	**24** 9:00 Coffee Group 2:00 Bird Feeding & Watching 6:00 Movie
25 9:00 Coffee Group 2:00 Church 6:00 Movie	**26** 9:00 Bedside Act. (9-11) 11:30 Exercise 2:00 Bible Study 3:00 Hospitality Club	**27** 10:00 Do You Remember? 11:30 President Quiz 2:00 Craft Club (Valentines)	**28** 9:00 Bedside Act. (9-11) 11:30 Exercise 11:45 Devotions 2:00 Bingo 6:00 Evening Movie	**29** 9:00am Beauty Club 11:30am President's Quiz 3:00pm Catholic Mass 6:00pm Movie		

March

Sunday	Monday	Tuesday	Wednesday	Thursday	Friday	Saturday
					1 9:00 Coffee & Newspaper 11:30 Exercise 11:45 Devotions 2:00 Rhythm Band	**2** 9:00 Coffee Group 2:00 Plant Care 6:00 Movie
3 9:00 Coffee Group 2:00 Church Family Visits	**4** 9:00 Bedside Act. (9-11) 11:30 Exercise 2:00 Bible Study 3:00 Sewing Club (Mending) 6:00 Band	**5** 10:00 Do You Remember? 11:30 Old Products 11:45 Devotions 2:00 Craft Club (Shamrocks)	**6** 9:00 Bedside Act. (9-11) 11:30 Exercise 11:45 Devotions 2:00 Bingo	**7** 9:00 Beauty Club (9-11) 11:30 States & Capitals 2:00 History Club 3:00 Catholic Mass	**8** 10:00 Tape Listening 11:30 Exercise 11:45 Devotions 3:00 History Club	**9** 9:00 Coffee Group 2:00 Old Radio 6:00 Checkers & Scrabble
10 9:00 Coffee Group 2:00 Church 3:00 Scrabble	**11** 9:00 Bedside Act. (9-11) 11:30 Exercise 2:00 Horticulture Club (Bottle Garden)	**12** 10:00 Do You Remember? 11:30 Food Quiz 2:30 Cooking Club (Mini-Pizzas) 6:00 Social Hour	**13** 9:00 Bedside Act. (9-11) 11:30 Exercise 11:45 Devotions 2:00 Bingo 6:00 Band	**14** 9:00 Beauty Club (9-11) 11:30 Word Game 2:00 Euchre 3:00 Catholic Mass	**15** 11:30 Exercise 11:45 Devotions 2:00 Bingo 6:00 Movie	**16** 9:00 Coffee Group 2:00 Plant Care 6:00 Movie
17 9:00 Coffee Group 2:00 Church 6:00 Old Radio	**18** 9:00 Bedside Act. (9-11) 11:30 Exercise 2:00 Bible Study 3:00 Hospitality Club	**19** 10:00 Do You Remember 11:30 Old Proverbs 2:00 Resident Council 6:00 Social Hour	**20** 9:00 Bedside Act. (9-11) 11:30 Exercise 11:45 Devotions 6:00 Evening Movie	**21** 9:00 Beauty Club (9-11) 11:30 Jokes & Riddles 2:00 Sing-A-Long 3:00 Catholic Mass	**22** 9:00 Music Appreciation (9-11) 11:30 Exercise 1:00 Outing Antique Shop	**23** 9:00 Coffee Group 2:00 Bird Feeding & Watching 6:00 Movie
24 9:00 Coffee Group 2:00 Church 6:00 Movie	**25** 9:00 Bedside Act. (9-11) 11:30 Exercise 11:45 Devotions 2:00 Literary Club	**26** 10:00 Do You Remember? 11:30 Spelling Bee 2:00 Arm-Chair Travel 6:00 Wine & Cheese	**27** 9:00 Bedside Act. (9-11) 11:30 Exercise 11:45 Devotions 6:00 Bingo	**28** 9:00 Beauty Club (9-11) 11:30 Current Events 2:00 Men's Club 3:00 Catholic Mass 7:00 Social Hour	**29** 10:00 Reading Group 2:00 Basketball Game 2:00 Exercise	**30** 9:00 Coffee Group 2:00 Plant Care 6:00 Movie
31 9:00 Coffee Group 2:00 Church 6:00 Movie						

April

Sunday	Monday	Tuesday	Wednesday	Thursday	Friday	Saturday
	1 9:00 Bedside Act 11:30 Exercise 11:45 Devotions 2:00 Literary Club	**2** 10:00 Do You Remember 11:30 Old Cars 11:45 Devotions 2:00 Craft Club (Easter Bonnets)	**3** 9:00 Bedside Act. (9-11) 11:30 Exercise 11:45 Devotions 2:00 Bingo	**4** 9:00 Beauty Club (9-11) 11:30 Nursery Rhymes 2:00 History Club (Kennedy) 3:00 Catholic Mass 7:00 Social Hour	**5** 9:00 Coffee & Newspaper 11:30 Exercise 11:45 Devotions 2:00 Rhythm Band	**6** 9:00 Coffee Group 2:00 Plant Care 6:00 Movie
7 9:00 Coffee Group 2:00 Church Family Visits	**8** 9:00 Bedside Act (9-11) 11:30 Exercise 2:00 Bible Study 3:00 Sewing Club (Aprons)	**9** 10:00 Do You Remember? 11:30 Superstitions 2:00 Cooking Club (Granola Bars) 6:00 Social Hour	**10** 9:00 Bedside Act (9-11) 11:30 Exercise 11:45 Devotions 2:00 Bingo 6:00 Band	**11** 9:00 Beauty Club (9-11) 11:30 Jokes & Riddles 2:00 Protestant Communion 3:00 Catholic Mass	**12** 9:00 Coffee & Newspaper 11:30 Exercise 2:00 Magazine Scavenger Hunt	**13** 9:00 Coffee Group 2:00 Old Radio 6:00 Checkers & Scrabble
14 9:00 Coffee Group 2:00 Church 3:00 Scramble	**15** 9:00 Bedside Act (9-11) 11:30 Exercise 2:00 Horticulture Club (Plant Bulbs)	**16** 10:00 Do You Remember? 11:30 Nursery Rhymes 2:00 Resident Council 6:00 Social Hour	**17** 9:00 Bedside Act (9-11) 11:30 Exercise 11:45 Devotions 2:00 Quilt Show 6:00 Evening Movie	**18** 9:00 Beauty Club (9-11) 11:30 History Quiz 3:00 Catholic Mass 6:00 Movie	**19** 10:00 Reading Group 11:30 Exercise 2:00 Basketball Game	**20** 9:00 Coffee Group 2:00 Plant Care 6:00 Movie
21 9:00 Coffee Group 2:00 Church 6:00 Old Radio	**22** 9:00 Bedside Act 11:30 Exercise 2:00 Bible Study 3:00 Hospitality Club	**23** 10:00 Do You Remember? 11:30 Similes 2:00 Birthday Party 6:00 Wine & Cheese	**24** 9:00 Bedside Act (9-11) 11:30 Exercise 11:45 Devotions 2:00 Bingo	**25** 9:00 Beauty Club (9-11) 11:30 Word Games 2:00 Puppet Show 3:00 Catholic Mass	**26** 10:00 Tape Listening 11:30 Exercise 11:45 Devotions 3:00 History club	**27** 9:00 Coffee Group 2:00 Bird Feeding & Watching 6:00 Movie
28 9:00 Coffee Group 2:00 Church 6:00 Movie	**29** 9:00 Bedside Act 11:30 Exercise 2:00 Birthday Party	**30** 10:00 Do You Remember? 11:30 N Y Quiz 2:00 Cooking Club 6:00 Social Hour				

May

Sunday	Monday	Tuesday	Wednesday	Thursday	Friday	Saturday
			1 9:00 Bedside Act. (9-11) 11:30 Exercise 11:45 Devotions 2:00 Bingo	**2** 9:00 Beauty Club (9-11) 2:00 Sing-A-Long 3:00 Catholic Mass 6:00 Movie	**3** 9:00 Coffee & Newspaper 11:30 Exercise 11:45 Devotions 2:00 Rhythm Band	**4** 9:00 Coffee Group 2:00 Old Radio 6:00 Checkers & Scrabble
5 9:00 Coffee Group 2:00 Church 3:00 Scrabble	**6** 9:00 Bedside Act. (9-11) 11:30 Exercise 2:00 Bible Study 3:00 Sewing Club	**7** 10:00 Do You Remember? 11:30 Old Products 11:45 Devotions 2:00 Craft Chmb (Fans)	**8** 9:00 Bedside Act (9-11) 11:30 Exercise 11:45 Devotions 2:00 Bingo	**9** 9:00 Beauty Club (9-11) 11:30 States & Capitals 2:00 Foot Swim 3:00 Catholic Mass 7:00 Social Hour	**10** 10:00 Tape Listening 11:30 Exercise 11:45 Devotions 3:00 History Club	**11** 9:00 Coffee Group 2:00 Plant Care 6:00 Movie
12 9:00 Coffee Group 2:00 Church 6:00 Old Radio	**13** 9:00 Bedside Act. (9-11) 11:30 Exercise 2:00 Horticulture Club (Outside Flower Box Planting)	**14** 10:00 Do You Remember? 11:30 History Quiz 2:00 Cooking Club (Strawberry Sundaes) 6:00 Social Hour	**15** 9:00 Bedside Act (9-11) 11:30 Exercise 11:45 Devotions 2:00 Bingo 6:00 Band	**16** 9:00 Beauty Club (9-11) 11:30 Jokes & Riddles 2:00 Nursery Rhymes 3:00 Catholic Mass	**17** 9:00 Music Appreciation (9-11) 11:30 Exercise 1:00 Joint Nursing Home Olympics (1-3)	**18** 9:00 Coffee Group 2:00 Bird Feeding & Watching 6:00 Movie
19 9:00 Coffee Group 2:00 Church 6:00 Movie	**20** 9:00 Bedside Act (9-11) 11:30 Exercise 2:00 Bible Study 3:00 Hospitality Club	**21** 10:00 Do You Remember? 11:30 Math Quiz 2:00 Resident Council 6:00 Social Hour	**22** 9:00 Bedside Act (9-11) 11:30 Exercise 11:45 Devotions 6:00 Evening Movie	**23** 9:00 Beauty Club (9-11) 11:30 Word Games 3:00 Catholic Mass	**24** 10:00 Story Group 11:30 Exercise 11:45 Devotions 2:00 Movie	**25** 9:00 Coffee Group 2:00 Plant Care 6:00 Movie
26 9:00 Coffee Group 2:00 Church 6:00 Movie	**27** 9:00 Bedside Act 11:30 Exercise 2:00 Birthday Party	**28** 10:00 Do You Remember? 11:30 20 Questions 2:00 Coupon Clipping 6:00 Wine & Cheese	**29** 9:00 Bedside Act (-11) 11:30 Exercise 11:45 Devotions 2:00 Bingo	**30** 9:00 Beauty Club (9-11) 11:30 Food Quiz 2:00 Yatzee 3:00 Catholic Mass	**31** 9:00 Music Appreciation (9-11) 11:30 Exercise 1:00 Outing Newspaper Tour	

June

Sunday	Monday	Tuesday	Wednesday	Thursday	Friday	Saturday
						1 9:00 Coffee Group 2:00 Bird Feeding & Watching 6:00 Movie
2 9:00 Coffee Group 2:00 Church Family Visits	**3** 10:00 Do You Remember? 11:45 Devotions 2:00 Clown Visit	**4** 9:00 Bedside Act. (9-11) 11:30 Exercise 2:00 Bible Study 3:00 Sewing Club (Baby Gowns)	**5** 9:00 Bedside Act. (9-11) 11:30 Exercise 11:45 Devotions 2:00 Bingo	**6** 9:00 Beauty Club (9-11) 11:30 Spelling Bee 2:00 Yarn Winding 3:00 Catholic mass	**7** 9:00 Coffee & Newspaper 11:30 Exercise 11:45 Devotions 2:00 Rhythm Band	**8** 9:00 Coffee Group 2:00 Plant Care 6:00 Movie
9 9:00 Coffee Group 2:00 Church 6:00 Old Radio	**10** 9:00 Bedside Act. (9-11) 11:30 Exercise 2:00 Horticulture Club (Plant Care)	**11** 10:00 Do You Remember? 11:30 Old Sayings 11:45 Devotions 2:00 Craft Club (Fabric Flowers)	**12** 9:00 Bedside Act. (9-11) 11:30 Exercise 11:45 Devotions 2:00 Bingo	**13** 9:00 Beauty Club (9-11) 11:30 Nursery Rhymes 2:00 Movie 3:00 Catholic Mass 7:00 Social Hour	**14** 10:00 Tape Listening 11:30 Exercise 11:45 Devotions 3:00 History Club (Lincoln)	**15** 9:00 Coffee Group 2:00 Plant care 6:00 Movie
16 9:00 Coffee Group 2:00 Church 3:00 Scrabble	**17** 9:00 Bedside Act. (9-11) 11:30 Exercise 11:45 Devotions 2:00 Literary Club (Book Reading)	**18** 10:00 Do You Remember? 11:30 Inventors 2:00 Resident Council 6:00 Social Hour	**19** 9:00 Bedside Act (9-11) 11:30 Exercise 11:45 Devotions 2:00 Bingo 6:00 Band	**20** 9:00 Beauty Club (9-11) 11:30 Jokes & Riddles 2:00 Men's Club (Bowling) 3:00 Catholic Mass	**21** 10:00 Reading Group 11:30 Exercise: Bean Hunt 2:00 Basketball Game	**22** 9:00 Coffee Group 2:00 Old Radio 6:00 Checkers & Scrabble
23 9:00 Coffee Gourp 2:00 Church 6:00 Movie	**24** 9:00 Bedside Act (9-11) 11:30 Exercise 2:00 Bible Study 3:00 Hospitality Club	**25** 10:00 Do You Remember? 11:30 Tic Tac Toe 2:00 Birthday Party 6:00 Wine & Cheese	**26** 9:00 Bedside act (9-11) 11:30 Exercise 11:45 Devotions 6:00 Evening Movie	**27** 9:00 Coffee Group 9:00 Outing: Farm (Lunch & Tour) (9-3) 3:00 Catholic Mass	**28** 9:00 Music Appreciation (9-11) 11:30 Exercise 2:00 Bridal Show	**29** 9:00 Coffee Group 2:00 30's Records 6:00 Scrabble
30 9:00 Coffee Group 2:00 Church Family Visits						

July

Sunday	Monday	Tuesday	Wednesday	Thursday	Friday	Saturday
	1 9:00 Bedside Act. (9-11) 11:30 Exercise 2:00 Doll Show 7:00 Church Group	**2** 10:00 Do You Remember? 11:45 Devotions 2:00 Art Show	**3** 9:00 Bedside Act. (9-11) 11:30 Exercise 11:45 Devotions 3:00 Mini-County Fair	**4** 9:00 Beauty Club (9-11) 11:30 Food Fun 2:00 Price is Right 3:00 Catholic Mass	**5** 10:00 Tape Listening 11:30 Exercise 11:45 Devotions 3:00 History Club (Immigration)	**6** 9:00 Coffee Group 2:00 Plant care 6:00 Movie
7 9:00 Coffee Group 2:00 Church Family Visits	**8** 9:00 Bedside Act. (9-11) 11:30 Exercise 2:00 Bible Study 3:00 Sewing CLub (Mending)	**9** 10:00 Do You Remember? 11:30 Math Quiz 2:00 Cook Club (Ice Cream) 6:00 Social Hour	**10** 9:00 Bedside Act (9-11) 11:30 Exercise 11:45 Devotions 2:00 Bingo 6:00 Band	**11** 9:00 Beauty Club (9-11) 11:30 Bible Quiz 2:00 Bingo 3:00 Catholic Mass 7:00 Social Hour	**12** 9:00 Music Appreciation (9-11) 11:30 Exercise 1:00 Outing : Park	**13** 9:00 Coffee Group 2:00 Old Radio 6:00 Checkers & Scrabble
14 9:00 Coffee Group 2:00 Church 3:00 Scrabble	**15** 9:00 Bedside Act (9-11) 11:30 Exercise 2:00 Horticulture Club (Flower Boxes)	**16** 10:00 Do You Remember? 11:30 20 Questions 2:00 Resident Council 6:00 Social Hour	**17** 9:00 Bedside Act (9-11) 11:30 Exercise 11:45 Devotions 2:00 Bingo 6:00 Evening Movie	**18** 9:00 Beauty Club (9-11) 11:30 Jokes & Riddles 2:00 Slide Show 3:00 Catholic Mass	**19** 10:00 Reading Group 11:30 Exercise 2:00 Basketball Game	**20** 9:00 Coffee Group 2:00 Plant Care 6:00 Movie
21 9:00 Coffee Group 2:00 Church 6:00 Movie	**22** 9:00 Bedside Act. (9-11) 11:30 Exercise 2:00 Bible Study 3:00 Hospitality Club	**23** 10:00 Do You Remember? 11:30 Bird Quiz 2:00 Birthday Party 6:00 Wine & Cheese	**24** 9:00 Bedside Act (9-11) 11:30 Exercise 11:45 Devotions 2:00 Bingo	**25** 9:00 Beauty Club (9-11) 11:30 Word Games 2:00 Badminton 3:00 Catholic Mass	**26** 9:00 Music Appreciation (9-11) 11:30 Exercise 2:00 Arthur Murray Dancers	**27** 9:00 Coffee Group 2:00 Bird Feeding & Watching 6:00 Movie
28 9:00 Coffee Group 2:00 Church 6:00 Old Radio	**29** 9:00 Bedside Act. (9-11) 11:30 Exercise 11:45 Devotions 2:00 Literary Club (Library Visit)	**30** 10:00 Do You Remember? 11:30 Patriotic Quiz 11:45 Devotions 2:00 Craft Club (Decoupage)	**31** 9:00 Bedside Act (9-11) 11:30 Exercise 11:45 Devotions 2:00 Bingo			

4th of July

August

Summer

Sunday	Monday	Tuesday	Wednesday	Thursday	Friday	Saturday
				1 9:00 Beauty Club (9-11) 11:30 Old Proverbs 2:00 Shoe Polishing 3:00 Catholic Mass	**2** 9:00 Coffee & Newspaper 11:30 Exercise 11:45 Devotions 2:00 Rhythm Band	**3** 9:00 Coffee Group 2:00 Plant Care 6:00 Movie
4 9:00 Coffee Group 2:00 Church Family Visits	**5** 9:00 Bedside Act. (9-11) 11:30 Exercise 2:00 Bible study 3:00 Sewing Club 7:00 Movie	**6** 10:00 Do You Remember? 11:45 Devotions 2:00 Paper Potluck	**7** 9:00 Bedside Act (9-11) 11:30 Exercise 11:45 Devotions 2:00 Bingo	**8** 9:00 Beauty Club 11:30 Price is Right 2:00 Singer 3:00 Catholic Mass 7:00 Social Hour	**9** 10:00 Tape Listening 11:30 Exercise 11:45 Devotions 3:00 History Club	**10** 9:00 Coffee Group 2:00 Old Radio 6:00 Checkers & Scrabble
11 9:00 Coffee Group 2:00 Church 3:00 Scrabble 6:00 Checkers & Scrabble	**12** 9:00 Bedside Act. (9-11) 11:30 Exercise 7:00 Ship Party (Families Invited)	**13** 10:00 Do You Remember? 11:30 Patriotic Games 11:45 Devotions 2:00 Craft Club (Noodle Jewelry)	**14** 9:00 Bedside Act (9-11) 11:30 Exercise 11:45 Devotions 2:00 Bingo	**15** 9:00 Beauty Club (9-11) 11:30 Jokes & Riddles 2:00 Paper Fashions 3:00 Catholic Mass	**16** 9:00 Music Appreciation (9-11) 11:30 Exercise Outing Creek (Wading)	**17** 9:00 Coffee Group 2:00 Plant Care 6:00 Movie
18 9:00 Coffee Group 2:00 Church 6:00 Old Radio	**19** 9:00 Bedside Act. (9-11) 11:30 Exercise 11:45 Devotions 2:00 Literary CLub	**20** 10:00 Do You Remember? 11:30 Nursery Rhymes 2:00 Resident Council 6:00 Social Hour	**21** 9:00 Bedside Act (9-11) 11:30 Exercise 11:45 Devotions 2:00 Bingo 6:00 Band	**22** 9:00 Beauty Club (9-11) 11:30 Word Games 3:00 Catholic Mass Patio Sitting	**23** 10:00 Reading Group 11:30 Exercise 2:00 Basketball Game	**24** 9:00 Coffee Group 2:00 Bird Feeding & Watching 6:00 Movie
25 9:00 Coffee Group 2:00 Church 6:00 Movie	**26** 9:00 Bedside Act. (9-11) 11:30 Exercise 2:00 Bible Study 3:00 Hospitality Club	**27** 10:00 Do You Remember? 11:30 Bible Quiz 2:00 Birthday Party 7:00 Wine & Cheese	**28** 9:00 Bedside Act (9-11) 11:30 Exercise 11:45 Devotions 6:00 Evening Movie	**29** 9:00 Beauty Club (9-11) 2:00 Story Group 3:00 Catholic	**30** 9:00 Coffee & Newspaper 11:30 Exercise 11:45 Devotions 2:00 Rhythm Band	**31** 9:00 Coffee Group 2:00 Plant Care 6:00 Movie

September

Sunday	Monday	Tuesday	Wednesday	Thursday	Friday	Saturday
1 9:00 Coffee Group 2:00 Church Family Visits	**2** 9:00 Bedside Act. (9-11) 11:30 Exercise 2:00 Bible Study 3:00 Sewing Club (Pot Holders)	**3** 0:00 Do You Remember? 11:30 Old Car Quiz 11:45 Devotions 2:00 Craft Club (Bottle Craft)	**4** 9:00 Bedside Act (9-11) 11:30 Exercise 11:45 Devotions 2:00 Bingo	**5** 9:00 Beauty Club (9-11) 11:30 Spelling Bee 2:00 Sing-A-Long 3:00 Catholic Mass	**6** 9:00 Coffee & Newspaper 11:30 Exercise 11:45 Devotions 2:00 Rhythm Band	**7** 9:00 Coffee Group 2:00 Plant Care 6:00 Movie
8 9:00 Coffee Group 2:00 Church 3:00 Scrabble	**9** 9:00 Bedside Act. (9-11) 11:30 Exercise 11:45 Devotions 2:00 Literary Club Speaker - Lit Teacher	**10** 10:00 Do You Remember? 11:30 History Quiz 2:00 Cooking Club (No Bake Cookies) 6:00 Social Hour	**11** 9:00 Bedside Act (9-11) 11:30 Exercise 11:45 Devotions 2:00 Bingo	**12** 9:00 Beauty Club (9-11) 2:00 Men's Club Dice Game 3:00 Catholic Mass 7:00 Social Hour	**13** 10:00 Tape Listening 11:30 Exercise 11:45 Devotions 3:00 History Club	**14** 9:00 Coffee Group 2:00 Old Radio 6:00 Checkers & Scrabble
15 9:00 Coffee Group 2:00 Church 6:00 Movie	**16** 9:00 Bedside Act (9-11) 11:30 Exercise 2:00 Bible Study 3:00 Hospitality Club	**17** 10:00 Do You Remember? 11:30 Old Proverbs 2:00 Resident Council 6:00 Social Hour	**18** 9:00 Bedside Act (9-11) 11:30 Exercise 11:45 Devotions 2:00 Bingo 6:00 Band	**19** 9:00 Beauty Club (9-11) 11:30 Jokes & Riddles 2:00 Horse Racing 3:00 Catholic Mass	**20** 2:00 Milking Contest/Hog Calling 6:00 Square Dancers Western Day Chuck Wagon Lunch Family	**21** 9:00 Coffee Group 2:00 Plant Care 6:00 Movie
22 9:00 Coffee Group 2:00 Church 6:00 Old Radio	**23** 9:00 Bedside Act (9-11) 11:30 Exercise 2:00 Horticulture Club (Plant Care)	**24** 10:00 Do You Remember? 11:30 Measurements 2:00 Birthday Party 7:00 Wine & Cheese	**25** 9:00 Bedside Act (9-11) 11:30 Exercise 11:45 Devotions 6:00 Evening Movie	**26** 9:00 Beauty Club (9-11) 11:30 Word Games 2:00 Movie 3:00 Catholic Mass	**27** 9:00 Music Appreciation (9-11) 11:30 Exercise 1:00 Outing Bus Tour of City	**28** 9:00 Coffee Group 2:00 Bird Feeding & Watching 6:00 Movie
29 9:00 Coffee Group 2:00 Church 6:00 Movie	**30** 9:00 Bedside Act (9-11) 11:30 Exercise School Class (Making Mural)					

Sunday	Monday	Tuesday	Wednesday	Thursday	Friday	Saturday
		1 10:00 Do You Remember? 11:30 States & Capital 11 45 Devotions 2:00 Craft Club (Horn of Plenty)	2 9 00 Bedside Act (9-11) 11 30 Exercise 11 45 Devotions 2:00 Bingo	3 9:00 Beauty Club (9-11) 11 30 Bird Quiz 2:00 Cake Dec. Demo 3:00 Catholic Mass 7:00 Social Hour	4 10:00 Tape Listening 11 30 Exercise 11 45 Devotions 3:00 History Club	5 9:00 Coffee Group 2:00 Plant Care 6:00 Movie
6 9:00 Coffee Group 2:00 Church Family Visits	7 9:00 Bedside Act (9-11) 11 30 Exercise 2:00 Bible Study 3:00 Sewing Club (Free Sew)	8 10:00 Do You Remember? 11:30 Old Proverbs 2:00 Cooking Club (Pumpkin Pies) 6:00 Social Hour	9 9:00 Bedside Act (9-11) 11 30 Exercise 11 45 Devotions 2:00 Bingo 6:00 Band	10 9:00 Beauty Club (9-11) 11:30 Jokes & Riddles 2:00 Slides Show 3 00 Catholic Mass	11 9:00 Music Appreciation (9-11) 11:30 Exercise 1 00 Outing Ride in County to see Leaves	12 9:00 Coffee Group 2:00 Old Radio 6:00 Checker & Scrabble
13 9:00 Coffee Group 2:00 Church 3:00 Scrabble	14 9:00 Bedside Act (9-11) 11 30 Exercise 2:00 Horticulture Club (Collect Leaves for Pressing)	15 10:00 Do You Remember? 11 30 Old Car Quiz 2:00 Resident Council 6:00 Social Hour	16 9:00 Bedside Act (9-11) 11 30 Exercise 11 45 Devotions 2:00 Bingo 6:00 Evening Movie	17 9:00 Beauty Club (9-11) 11 30 Word Games 2:00 Library Visit 3:00 Catholic Mass 7:00 Wine & Cheese Party	18 10:00 Reading Group 11 30 Exercise Bear Hunt 2:00 Basketball Game	19 9:00 Coffee Group 2:00 Plant Care 6:00 Movie
20 9:00 Coffee Group 2:00 Church 6:00 Old Radio	21 9:00 Bedside Act (9-11) 11 30 Exercise 2:00 Bible Study 3:00 Hospitality Club	22 10:00 Do You Remember? 11 30 Song Titles 7:00 Wine & Cheese	23 9:00 Bedside Act (9 1 11 30 Exercise 11 45 Devotions 2:00 Bingo	24 9:00 Beauty Club (9-11) 11:30 Smiles 2 00 Arm Lunches 3 00 Catholic Mass	25 9:00 Coffee Group 2:00 4:00 Fall Festival (School Class Invited)	26 9:00 Coffee Group 2:00 Bird Feeding & Watching 6:00 Movie
27 9:00 Coffee Group 2 00 Church 6:00 Movie	28 9:00 Bedside Act (9-11) 11 40 Exercise 11 45 Devotions 2 00 Literary Club	29 9:00 Coffee & Newspaper 11 30 Exercise 11 45 Devotions 2 00 Rhythm Band	30 9:00am Bedside Act 11 30am Exercise 11 45am Devotions 2:00pm Bingo	31 9:00 Beauty Club (9-11) 2 00 Ballroom Volley ball 3 00 Catholic Mass		

November

Sunday	Monday	Tuesday	Wednesday	Thursday	Friday	Saturday
					1 9:00 Coffee & Newspaper 11:30 Exercise 11:45 Devotions 2:00 Rhythm Band	**2** 9:00 Coffee Group 2:00 Plant Care 6:00 Movie
3 9:00 Coffee Group 2:00 Church Family Visits	**4** 9:00 Bedside Act. (9-11) 11:30 Exercise 2:00 Bible Study 3:00 Sewing Club (Sewing Doll)	**5** 10:00 Do You Remember? 11:30 Math Quiz 11:45 Devotions 2:00 Craft Club (Prune Turkeys)	**6** 9:00 Bedside Act. 11:30 Exercise 11:45 Devotions 2:00 Bingo	**7** 9:00 Beauty Club (9-11) 11:30 Presidents 2:00 Pizza Party 3:00 Catholic Mass	**8** 10:00 Tape Listening 11:30 Exercise 11:45 Devotions 3:00 History Club	**9** 9:00 Coffee Group 2:00 Old Radio 6:00 Checkers & Scrabble
10 9:00 Coffee Group 2:00 Church 3:00 Scrabble	**11** 9:00 Bedside Act. (9-11) 11:30 Exercise 2:00 Bible Study 3:00 Hospitality Club	**12** 10:00 Do You Remember? 10:00 President Quiz 2:00 Cooking Club (Oyster Soup) 6:00 Social Hour	**13** 9:00 Bedside Act. (9-11) 11:30 Exercise 11:45 Devotions 2:00 Bingo	**14** 9:00 Beauty Club (9-11) 11:30 Bird Quiz 2:00 Show and Tell 3:00 Catholic Mass 7:00 Social Hour	**15** 9:00 Music Appreciation (9-11) 11:30 Exercise 1:00 Outing Ice Cream Parlor	**16** 9:00 Coffee Group 2:00 Plant Care 6:00 Movie
17 9:00 Coffee Group 2:00 Church 2:00 Old Radio	**18** 9:00 Bedside Act. (9-11) 11:30 Exercise 11:45 Devotions 2:00 Literary Club	**19** 10:00 Do You Remember? 11:30 20 Questions 2:00 Resident Council 6:00 Social Hour	**20** 9:00 Bedside Act (9-11) 11:30 Exercise 11:45 Devotions 2:00 Bingo 6:00 Band	**21** 9:00 Beauty Club (9-11) 11:30 Jokes & Riddles 2:00 Nut Packing 3:00 Catholic Mass	**22** 10:00 Reading Group 11:30 Exercise 2:00 Basketball Game	**23** 9:00 Coffee Group 2:00 Bird Feeding & Watching 6:00 Movie
24 9:00 Coffee Group 2:00 Church 6:00 Movie	**25** 9:00 Bedside Act. (9-11) 11:30 Exercise 2:00 Horticulture Club (Natural Tree Decorations)	**26** 10:00 Do You Remember? 11:30 History Quiz 2:00 Birthday Party	**27** 9:00 Bedside Act (9-11) 11:30 Exercise 11:45 Devotions 2:00 Bingo 6:00 Evening Movie	**28** 9:00 Beauty Club (9-11) 11:30 Word Games 2:00 Photo Sharing 3:00 Catholic Mass	**29** 9:00 Coffee & Newspaper 11:30 Exercise 11:45 Devotions 2:00 Rhythm Band	**30** 9:00am Coffee Group 2:00pm Plant Care 6:00pm Movie

December

Sunday	Monday	Tuesday	Wednesday	Thursday	Friday	Saturday
1 Family Visits 9:00am Coffee Group 2:00pm Church	**2** 9:00 Bedside Act. (9-11) 11:30 Exercise 2:00 Bible study 3:00 Sewing CLub (Doll House Curtains & Rugs)	**3** 10:00 Do You Remember? 11:45 Devotions 2:00 Craft Club 7:00 Doll House	**4** 9:00 Coffee Group 6:00 Christmas Movie Decorate Facility (All Day)	**5** 9:00 Beauty Club (9-11) 11:30 Reindeer Game 2:00 Decorate Tree 3:00 Catholic Mass	**6** 10:00 Tape Listening 11:30 Exercise 11:45 Devotions 3:00 History Club (St. Nick)	**7** 9:00 Coffee Group 2:00 Plant Care 6:00 Movie
8 9:00 Coffee Group 2:00 Church 3:00 Paint Doll House Furniture	**9** 9:00 Bedside Act. (9-11) 11:30 Exercise 2:00 Horticulture Club (Make Tiny Plants for Doll House)	**10** 10:00 Do You Remember? 11:30 Christmas Quiz 2:00 Cooking Club (Popcorn Balls) 6:00 Social Hour	**11** 9:00 Bedside Act (9-11) 11:30 Exercise 11:45 Devotions 2:00 Nursery School Christmas Play	**12** 9:00 Work on Doll House (9-11) 2:00 Sing-A-Long 3:00 Catholic Mass 7:00 Social Hour	**13** 9:00 Music Appreciation (9-11) 11:30 Exercise Christmas Shopping (In-House)	**14** 9:00 Coffee Group 2:00 Old Radio 7:00 Carollers Work on Doll House
15 9:00 Coffee Group 2:00 Church 3:00 Carollers	**16** 9:00 Bedside Act. (9-11) 11:30 Exercise 2:00 Bible Study 3:00 Hospitality Club	**17** 9:00 Bedside Act. (9-11) 11:30 Exercise 2:00 Finish Doll House 6:00 Christmas Movie	**18** 9:00 Bedside Act (9-11) 11:30 Exercise 11:45 Devotions 2:00 Bingo 6:00 Band	**19** 9:00 Beauty Club (9-11) 11:30 Jokes & Riddles 2:00 Christmas Movie 3:00 Catholic Mass	**20** 10:00 Reading Group 2:00 Christmas Party 7:00 Social Hour	**21** 9:00 Coffee Group 2:00 Doll House 6:00 Carollers
22 9:00 Coffee Group 2:00 Church 5:00 Carollers	**23** 9:00 Bedside Act. (9-11) 11:30 Exercise 11:45 Devotions 2:00 Literary Club Night Before Christmas Poem	**24** 9:00 Resident Pancake Fry 11:30 Holiday Quiz 2:00 Resident Council 6:00 Social Hour	**25** Christmas Dinner 6:00 PM Movie	**26** 9:00 Beauty Club 11:30 Word Games 2:00 Doll House Drawing & Give-Away 3:00 Christmas Community Service	**27** 9:00 Music Appreciation (9-11) 11:30 Presidents Review Year 2:00 Egg Nog & Tea	**28** 9:00 Coffee Group 10:00 Open Gifts 6:00 Christmas Movie
29 9:00 Coffee Group 2:00 Church 6:00 Movie	**30** 9:00am Bedside Act. 11:30am Exercise 2:00pm Bible Study 3:00pm Sewing Club 6:00pm Band	**31** 10:00 Do You Remember? 2:00 Basketball Game 7:00 Wine & Cheese				

January

Sunday	Monday	Tuesday	Wednesday	Thursday	Friday	Saturday
			1	**2** 9:00am Beauty Club 2:00pm Catholic Christmas Service 3:00pm Protestant Communion Service	**3** 9:00am Coffee & Newspaper 11:30am Exercise 11:45am Devotions 2:00pm Rhythm Band	**4** 9:00am Coffee Group 2:00pm Plant Care 6:00pm Movie
5 Family Visits 9:00am Coffee Group 2:00pm Church	**6** 9:00am Bedside Act 11:30am Exercise 11:45am Devotions 3:00pm Sewing Club (Pot Holders) 7:00pm Homemaker's Club	**7** 10:00am Do You Remember? 11:30am New York Quiz 2:00pm Craft Club (Bottled Beans) 6:00pm Guitar Player	**8** 9:00am Bedside Act 11:30am Exercise 11:45am Devotions 2:00pm Bingo 6:00pm Lincoln Logs Cabin Bldg	**9** 9:00am Beauty Club 11:30am Circus Quiz 2:00pm Toss Across 3:00pm Catholic Mass	**10** 9:00am Music Appreciation (9-11) 11:30am Exercise 1:00pm Outing Antique Store 6:00pm Social Hour	**11** 9:00am Coffee Group 2:00pm Cards 6:00pm Old Radio
12 Family Visits 9:00am Coffee Group 2:00pm Church 4:00pm Cards	**13** 9:00am Bedside Act 11:30am Exercise 2:00pm Hospitality Club (Planning Mtg.) 6:00pm Movie	**14** 10:00am Do You Remember? 11:30am Jokes & Riddles 2:00pm Hat Fun	**15** 9:00am Bedside Act 11:30am Exercise 11:45am Devotions 2:00pm Bingo 6:00pm Bragging Time	**16** 9:00am Beauty Club 11:45am State Capitals 2:00pm Movie 3:00pm Catholic Mass	**17** 9:00am Coffee Group 11:30am Exercise 2:00pm Name That Tune	**18** 9:00am Coffee Group 2:00pm Movie 6:00pm Jigsaw Puzzles
19 9:00am Coffee Group 2:00pm Church 2:00pm Old Radio Show	**20** 9:00am Bedside Act 11:30am Exercise 2:00pm School Visit 2:00pm Men's Club (Pilot Speaking)	**21** 10:00am Do You Remember? 11:30am Math Quiz 2:00pm Make Snow Ice Cream 6:00pm Movie	**22** 9:00am Bedside Act 11:30am Exercise 11:45am Devotions 2:00pm Bingo 7:00pm Wine & Cheese Party	**23** 9:00am Beauty Club 11:30am Famous Holidays 2:00pm Balloon Volleyball 3:00pm Catholic Mass	**24** 9:00am Music Appreciation (9-11) 11:30am Exercise 2:00pm Basketball Game	**25** 9:00am Coffee Group 2:00pm Plant Care 8:00pm Wheel of Fortune
26 9:00am Coffee Group 2:00pm Church 2:00pm Nut Cracking 6:00pm Movie	**27** 9:00am Bedside Act 11:30am Exercise 2:00pm Resident Council	**28** 10:00am Do You Remember? 2:00pm Beauty Make-Over 3:00pm Literary Club	**29** 9:00am Bedside Act 11:30am Exercise 11:45am Devotions 2:00pm Queen Contest 6:00pm Tic Tac Toe	**30** 9:00am Beauty Club 11:30am President Quiz 2:00pm Pizza Party 3:00pm Catholic Mass	**31** 9:00am Coffee & Newspaper 11:30am Exercise 11:45am Devotions	Happy Birthday!

February

Sunday	Monday	Tuesday	Wednesday	Thursday	Friday	Saturday
						1 9:00am Coffee Group 2:00pm Yarn Winding 6:00pm Checkers & Scrabble
2 9:00am Coffee Group 2:00pm Church 3:00pm Scrabble	**3** 9:00am Bedside Act. 11:30am Exercise 2:00pm Bible Study 3:00pm Hospitality CLub	**4** 10:00am Do You Remember? 11:45am Devotions 2:00pm Craft Club (Make Valentine Box)	**5** 9:00am Bedside Act. 11:30am Exercise 11:45am Devotions 2:00pm Bingo	**6** 9:00am Beauty Club 11:30am Spelling Bee 3:00pm Catholic Mass 7:00pm Social Hour	**7** 10:00am Tape Listening 11:30am Exercise 11:45am Devotions 3:00pm History Club	**8** 9:00am Coffee Group 2:00pm Plant Care 6:00pm Movie
9 9:00am Coffee Group 2:00pm Church 6:00pm Old Radio	**10** 9:00am Bedside Act. 11:30am Exercise 2:00pm Horticulture Club 7:00pm Gay Nineties Family Party	**11** 10:00am Do You Remember? 11:45am Patriotic Quiz 2:00pm Cooking Club (Valentine Cookies) 6:00pm Social Hour	**12** 9:00am Bedside Act. 11:30am Exercise 11:45am Devotions 2:00pm Bingo	**13** 9:00am Beauty Club 11:30am Jokes & Riddles 1:30pm Valentine Party 3:00pm Catholic Mass	**14** 9:00am Music Appreciation (9-11) 11:30am Exercise 1:00pm Outing: Library	**15** 9:00am Coffee Group 2:00pm Bird Feeding & Watching
16 9:00am Coffee Group 2:00pm Church 6:00pm Movie	**17** 9:00am Bedside Act. 11:30am Exercise 11:45am Devotions 2:00pm Literary Club	**18** 10:00am Do You Remember? 11:45am States & Capitals 2:00pm Resident Council 6:00pm Social Hour	**19** 9:00am Bedside Act. 11:30am Exercise 11:45am Devotions 2:00pm Bingo 6:00pm Evening Movie	**20** 9:00am Beauty Club 2:00pm Newsletter Mailing 3:00pm Catholic Mass	**21** 10:00am Reading Group 11:30am Exercise 2:00pm Basketball Game	**22** 9:00am Coffee Group 2:00pm Plant care 6:00pm Movie
23 Family Visits 9:00am Coffee Group 2:00pm Church	**24** 9:00am Bedside Act 11:30am Exercise 2:00pm Bible study 3:00pm Sewing Club 6:00pm Old Radio	**25** 10:00am Do You Remember? 2:00pm Sing A-Long 7:00pm Wine & Cheese	**26** 9:00am Bedside Act 11:30am Exercise 11:45am Devotions 2:00pm Shoe Polishing	**27** 9:00am Beauty Club 11:30am Food Quiz 3:00pm Catholic Mass 6:00pm Movie	**28** 9:00am Coffee & Newspaper 11:30am Exercise 11:45am Devotions 2:00pm Rhythm Band	

March

Sunday	Monday	Tuesday	Wednesday	Thursday	Friday	Saturday
						1 9:00am Coffee Group 2:00pm Old Radio 6:00pm Checkers & Scramble
2 9:00am Coffee Group 2:00pm Church 3:00pm Scramble	**3** 9:00am Bedside Act. 11:30am Exercise 2:00pm Bible Study 3:00pm Hospitality CLub	**4** 10:00am Do You Remember? 11:30am Split Infinitives 2:00pm Craft Club (Make Shamrocks)	**5** 9:00am Bedside Act. 11:30am Exercise 11:45am Devotions 2:00pm Bingo 6:00pm Band	**6** 9:00am Beauty Club 11:30am Old Measurements 3:00pm Catholic Mass	**7** 10:00am Tape Listening 11:30am Exercise 11:45am Devotions 3:00pm History CLub	**8** 9:00am Coffee Group 2:00pm Plant Care 6:00pm Movie
9 9:00am Coffee Group 2:00pm Church 6:00pm Old Radio	**10** 9:00am Bedside Act. 11:30am Exercise 2:00pm Horticulture Club 6:00pm Guitar Player	**11** 10:00am Do You Remember? 11:30am Flower Quiz 2:00pm Cooking Club 6:00pm Social Hour	**12** 9:00am Bedside Act. 11:30am Exercise 11:45am Devotions 6:00pm Evening Movie	**13** 9:00am Beauty Club 2:00pm Male Cotton Candy 3:00pm Catholic Mass 7:00pm Social Hour	**14** 10:00am Reading Group 11:30am Exercise 2:00pm Basketball game	**15** 9:00am Coffee Group 2:00pm Bird Feeding & Watching 6:00pm Movie
16 9:00am Coffee Group 2:00pm Church 6:00pm Movie	**17** 9:00am Music Appreciation (9-11) 11:30am Exercise 2:00pm St. Patrick's Birthday Party	**18** 10:00am Do You Remember? 11:30am Old Proverbs 2:00pm Resident Council 6:00pm Social Hour	**19** 9:00am Bedside Act. 11:30am Exercise 11:45am Devotions 2:00pm Bingo	**20** 9:00am Beauty Club 11:30am Jokes & Riddles 1:00pm Outing Hardees 3:00pm Catholic Mass	**21** 9:00am Music Appreciation (9-11) 11:30am Bear Hunt 11:45am Devotions 2:00pm Wild Game Hunt	**22** Family Visits 9:00am Coffee Group 2:00pm Piano
23 9:00am Coffee Group 2:00pm Church 6:00pm Movie	**24** 9:00am Bedside Act. 11:30am Exercise 2:00pm Literary Club	**25** 10:00am Do You Remember? 11:45am Superstitions 2:00pm Horse Shoe 7:00pm Wine & Cheese	**26** 9:00am Bedside Act. 11:30am Exercise 11:45am Devotions 2:00pm Bingo 7:00pm Barber Shop Quartet	**27** 9:00am Beauty Club 11:30am Word Games 2:00pm Movie 3:00pm Catholic Mass	**28** 10:00am Do You Remember? 11:30am Devotions 11:45am Old Proverbs 2:00pm Movie	**29** 9:00am Coffee Group 2:00pm Plant Care 6:00pm Movie/Cards
30 Family Visits 9:00am Coffee Group 2:00pm Church	**31** 9:00am Bedside Act. 11:30am Exercise 2:00pm Men's Pretty Leg Contest					

April

Sunday	Monday	Tuesday	Wednesday	Thursday	Friday	Saturday
Arbor Day		**1** 10:00am Do You Remember? 11:30am Spelling Bee 11:45am Devotions 2:00pm Craft Club (Paper Plate Bonnets)	**2** 9:00am Bedside Act. 11:30am Exercise 11:45am Devotions 2:00pm Bingo 2:00pm Bible Study	**3** 9:00am Beauty Club 11:30am Nursery Rhymes 2:00pm Card Cutting 3:00pm Catholic Mass 7:00pm Social Hour	**4** 10:00am Tape Listening 11:30am Exercise 11:45am Devotions 3:00pm History Club	**5** 9:00am Coffee Group 2:00pm Plant Care 6:00pm Movie
6 Family Visits 9:00am Coffee Group 2:00pm Church	**7** 9:00am Bedside Act. 11:30am Exercise 2:00pm Bible Study 3:00pm Sewing Club	**8** 10:00am Do You Remember? 2:00pm Cooking Club (Egg Salad) 6:00pm Social Hour	**9** 9:00am Bedside Act. 11:30am Exercise 11:45am Devotions 2:00pm Bingo 6:00pm Band	**10** 9:00am Beauty Club 11:30am Jokes & Riddles 2:00pm Euchre 3:00pm Catholic Mass	**11** 9:00am Music Appreciation (9-11) 11:30am Exercise 2:00pm Outing: Ride in Country	**12** 9:00am Coffee Group 2:00pm Old Radio 6:00pm Checkers & Scrabble
13 9:00am Coffee Group 2:00pm Church 3:00pm Scrabble	**14** 9:00am Bedside Act. 11:30am Exercise 2:00pm Horticulture Club	**15** 10:00am Do You Remember? 2:00pm Resident Council 6:00pm Social Hour	**16** 9:00am Bedside Act. 11:30am Exercise 11:45am Devotions 2:00pm Bingo 6:00pm Evening Movie	**17** 9:00am Beauty Club 11:30am Word Games 3:00pm Catholic Mass	**18** 10:00am Reading Group 11:30am Exercise 11:45am Devotions 2:00pm Basketball Game	**19** 9:00am Coffee Group 2:00pm Plant Care 6:00pm Movie
20 9:00am Coffee Group 2:00pm Church 6:00pm Old Radio	**21** 9:00am Bedside Act. 11:30am Exercise 2:00pm Bible Study 3:00pm Hospitality Club	**22** 10:00am Do You Remember? 2:00pm Baby Contest	**23** 9:00am Bedside Act 11:30am Exercise 11:45am Devotions 2:00pm Bingo	**24** 9:00am Beauty Club 11:30am Old Proverbs 2:00pm Cake Decorating Demo 3:00pm Catholic Mass	**25** 9:00am Coffee & Newspaper 11:30am Exercise 11:45am Devotions 2:00pm Rhythm Band	**26** 9:00am Coffee Group 2:00pm Bird Feeding & Watching 6:00pm Movie
27 9:00am Coffee Group 2:00pm Church 6:00pm Movie	**28** 9:00am Bedside Act. 11:30am Exercise 2:00pm Literary Club	**29** 9:00am Bedside Act. 11:30am Exercise 11:45am Devotions 2:00pm Horse Racing	**30** 10:00am Do You Remember? 10:30am Bird Quiz 11:45am Devotions 2:00pm Craft Club			

May

Sunday	Monday	Tuesday	Wednesday	Thursday	Friday	Saturday
				1 9:00am Beauty Club 11:30am Jokes & Riddles 2:00pm Rhythm Band 3:00pm Catholic Mass	**2** 10:00am Tape Listening 11:30am Exercise 3:00pm History Club	**3** 9:00am Coffee Group 2:00pm Plant Care 6:00pm Movie
4 9:00am Coffee Group 2:00pm Church 3:00pm Scrabble	**5** 9:00am Bedside Act. 11:30am Exercise 2:00pm Bible Study 3:00pm Sewing Club (Teddy Bears)	**6** 10:00am Do You Remember? 11:30am Name Game 11:45am Devotions 2:00pm Craft Club (Spool Totem Poles)	**7** 9:00am Bedside Act. 11:30am Exercise 11:45am Devotions 2:00pm Bingo	**8** 9:00am Beauty Club 11:30am Sound Alikes 2:00pm Photo Sharing 3:00pm Catholic Mass 7:00pm Social Hour	**9** 9:00am Music Appreciation (9-11) 11:30am Exercise 1:30pm Outing - Church Tour	**10** 9:00am Coffee Group 2:00pm Plant Care 6:00pm Movie/Cards
11 9:00am Coffee Group 2:00pm Church 6:00pm Old Radio	**12** Potato Grass Garden 9:00am Bedside Act. 11:30am Exercise 2:00pm Horticulture Club	**13** 10:00am Do You Remember? 11:30am Tongue Twisters 2:00pm Cooking Club (Butter) 6:00pm Social Hour	**14** 9:00am Bedside Act. 11:30am Exercise 11:45am Devotions 2:00pm Bingo 6:00pm Band	**15** 9:00am Beauty Club 11:30am Jokes & Riddles 1:30pm Men's Club (Tractor Show) 3:00pm Catholic Mass	**16** 10:00am Reading roup 11:30am Exercise 2:00pm Basketball Game	**17** 9:00am Coffee Group 2:00pm Bird Feeding & Watching 6:00pm Movie
18 9:00am Coffee Group 2:00pm Church 6:00pm Movie	**19** 9:00am Bedside Act 11:30am Exercise 11:45am Devotions 2:00pm Literary Club	**20** 10:00am Do You Remember? 11:30am 20 Questions 2:00pm Soap Bubble Fun 6:00pm Social Hour	**21** 9:00am Bedside Act. 11:30am Exercise 11:45am Devotions 2:00pm Bingo 6:00pm Evening Movie	**22** 9:00am Beauty Club 11:30am Word Games 3:00pm Catholic Mass	**23** 9:00am COffee roup 2:00pm Arthur Murray Dancers 6:00pm Movie	**24** 9:00am Coffee Group 2:00pm Old Radio 6:00pm Checkers & Scrabble
25 Family Visits 9:00am Coffee Group 2:00pm Church	**26** 9:00am Bedside Act. 11:30am Exercise 2:00pm Bible Study 3:00pm Sewing Club 6:00pm Band	**27** 10:00am Do You Remember? 11:30am Food Quiz 2:00pm Resident Council 7:00pm Wine & Cheese	**28** 9:00am Bedside Act. 11:30am Exercise 11:45am Devotions 2:00pm Bingo	**29** 9:00am Beauty Club 11:30am Famous Inventors 1:30pm Birthday Part 3:00pm Catholic Mass	**30** 9:00am Music Appreciation (9-11) 11:30am Exercise 11:45am Devotions 2:00pm Popcorn Party	**31** 9:00am Coffee Group 2:00pm Plant Care 6:00pm Movie

June

Sunday	Monday	Tuesday	Wednesday	Thursday	Friday	Saturday
1 9:00am Coffee Group 2:00pm Church 3:00pm Scrabble	**2** 9:00am Bedside Act. 11:30am Exercise 2:00pm Horticulture Club (Plant Seeds)	**3** 10:00am Do You Remember? 11:30am States & Capitals 1:00pm Nursing Home Olympics 6:00pm Social Hour	**4** 9:00am Bedside Act. 11:30am Exercise 11:45am Devotions 2:00pm Bridal Consultant Speak	**5** 9:00am Beauty Club 11:30am Old Proverbs 2:00pm Male Incubator 3:00pm Catholic Mass 7:00pm Social Hour	**6** Get Fertile Eggs 10:00am Tape Listening 11:30am Exercise 11:45am Devotions 3:00pm History Club	**7** 9:00am Coffee Group 2:00pm Old Radio 6:00pm Checkers & Scrabble
8 9:00am Coffee Group 2:00pm Church 2:00pm Old Radio	**9** 9:00am Bedside Act. 11:30am Exercise 2:00pm Bible Study 3:00pm Hospitality Club	**10** 10:00am Do You Remember? 11:30am New York Quiz 2:00pm Men's Club (Auto Racing Movie) 6:00pm Social Hour	**11** 9:00am Bedside Act. 11:30am Exercise 11:45am Devotions 2:00pm Bingo 6:00pm Band	**12** 9:00am Beauty Club 11 30am Word Game 2:00pm Horseshoe 3:00pm Catholic Mass	**13** 9:00am Music Appreciation (9-11) 11:30am Exercise 1:30pm Outing. Park	**14** 9:00am Coffee Group 2:00pm Plant Care 6:00pm Movie
15 9:00am Coffee Group 2:00pm Church 6:00pm Movie	**16** 9:00am Bedside Act. 11:30am Exercise 11:45am Devotions 2:00pm Literary Club	**17** 10:00am Do You Remember? 2:00pm Resident Council 6:00pm Birthday Celebration	**18** 9:00am Bedside Act. 11:30am Exercise 11:45am Devotions 2:00pm Bingo 6:00pm Evening Movie	**19** 9:00am Beauty Club 2:00pm Checker & Scrabble 3:00pm Catholic Mass	**20** 10:00am Reading Group 11:30am Exercise 2:00pm Basketball Game	**21** 9:00am Coffee Group 2:00pm Bird Feeding & Watching 6:00pm Movie
22 9:00am Coffee Group 2:00pm Church 6:00pm Movie	**23** 9:00am Bedside Act. 11:30am Exercise 2:00pm Movie 7:00pm Church Choir	**24** 10:00am Do You Remember? 11:45am Devotions 2:00pm Ice Cream Social 7:00pm Social Hour	**25** 9:00am Bedside Act. 11:30am Exercise 11:45am Devotions 2:00pm Bingo	**26** Watch Chicks Hatching 9:00am Beauty Club 3:00pm Catholic Mass 6:00pm Checker Tournament	**27** Watch Chicks Hatching 9:00am Music Appreciation (9-11) 6:00pm Arm Chair Travel Slides	**28** 9:00am Coffee Group 2:00pm Card Cutting 8:00pm Wheel of Fortune
29 Family Visits 9:00am Coffee Group 2:00pm Church 6:00pm Movie	**30** 9:00am Bedside Act. 11:30am Exercise 11:45am Devotions 2:00pm Bingo					

FATHER'S DAY

July

Sunday	Monday	Tuesday	Wednesday	Thursday	Friday	Saturday
		1 9:00am Bedside Act. 11:30am Exercise 2:00pm Horticulture Club (Tend Gardens)	**2** 9:00am Bedside Act. 11:30am Exercise 11:45am Devotions 2:00pm Pet Show (Community Invited)	**3** 9:00am Beauty Club 11:30am Spelling Bee 2:00pm Men's Club (Bowling) 3:00pm Catholic Mass 7:00pm Social Hour	**4** HAPPY 4TH OF JULY 9:00am Bedside Act. 11:30am Exercise 2:00pm Bible Study 3:00pm Movie	**5** 9:00am Coffee Group 2:00pm Old Radio 6:00pm Checkers & Scrabble
6 Family Visits 9:00am Coffee Group 2:00pm Church	**7** 10:00am Do You Remember? 11:30am Superstitions 11:45am Devotions 2:00pm Craft Club (Clown Hats)	**8** 9:00am Bedside Act. 11:30am Exercise 2:00pm Bible Study 3:00pm Hospitality CLub	**9** 9:00am Bedside Act. 11:30am Exercise 11:45am Devotions 2:00pm Bingo 6:00pm Band	**10** 9:00am Beauty Club 11:30am Jokes & Riddles 2:00pm Ballon Volleyball 3:00pm Catholic Mass	**11** 9:00am Coffee & Newspaper 11:30am Exercise 11:45am Devotions 2:00pm Rhythm Band	**12** 9:00am Coffee Group 2:00pm Plant Care 6:00pm Movie
13 9:00am Coffee Group 2:00pm Church 3:00pm Scrabble	**14** 10:00am Do You Remember? 11:30am Old Proverb 2:00pm Cooking CLub (Fruit Salad Making) 6:00pm Social Hour	**15** 9:00am Bedside Act. 11:30am Exercise 11:45am Devotions 2:00pm Literary Club (Discuss Famous Writers)	**16** 9:00am Bedside Act. 11:30am Exercise 11:45am Devotions 2:00pm Bingo 2:00pm Resident Council 6:00pm Evening Movie	**17** 9:00am Beauty Club 11:30am Word Games 2:00pm Guest Antique Collector 3:00pm Catholic Mass	**18** 10:00am Tape Listening 11:30am Exercise 11:45am Devotions 3:00pm History Club (Discuss 30's)	**19** 9:00am Coffee Group 2:00pm Bird Feeding & Watching 6:00pm Movie
20 9:00am Coffee Group 2:00pm Church 3:00pm Old Radio	**21** 10:00am Do You Remember? 11:30am Fill in the Blanks Quiz 2:00pm Resident Council 6:00pm Social Hour	**22** 9:00am Music Appreciation (9-11) 11:30am Exercise 1:00pm Outing Tour Police Station	**23** 9:00am Bedside Act. 11:30am Exercise 11:45am Devotions 2:00pm Bingo	**24** 9:00am Beauty Club 11:30am 20 Questions 2:00pm Bean Bag Fun 3:00pm Catholic Mass 6:00pm Social Hour	**25** 10:00am Reading Group 11:30am Exercise 2:00pm Basketball Game	**26** 9:00am Coffee Group 2:00pm Bird Feeding & Watching 3:00pm Scrabble
27 9:00am Coffee Group 2:00pm Church 6:00pm Movie	**28** 10:00am Do You Remember? 11:30am Holiday Quiz 2:00pm Piano Player 7:00pm Wine & Cheese	**29** 10:00am Do You Remember? 11:30am Auto Quiz 11:45am Devotions 2:00pm Cooking (Taffy Pull) 6:00pm Social Hour	**30** 9:00am Bedside Act 11:30am Exercise 11:45am Devotions 2:00pm Bingo	**31** 9:00am Beauty Club 11:30am Word Games 2:00pm Literary Club (Read Poems) 3:00pm Catholic Mass		

August

Sunday	Monday	Tuesday	Wednesday	Thursday	Friday	Saturday
					1 9:00am Music Appreciation (9-11) 10:00am -3:00 Outing: Fishing Trip & Luncheon 6:00pm Guitar Player	**2** 9:00am Coffee Group 2:00pm Popcorn Party 2:00pm Plant Care
3 9:00am Coffee Group 2:00pm Church 3:00pm Scrabble	**4** 9:00am Bedside Act. 11:30am Exercise 1:00pm Hospitality Club (Flower Arranging) 2:00pm Bible Study	**5** 10:00am Do You Remember? 11:30am Old Proverb 2:00pm Resident Council 6:00pm Band	**6** 9:00am Bedside Act. 11:30am Exercise 11:45am Devotions 2:00pm Bingo	**7** 9:00am Beauty Club 11:30am Famous People Quiz 11:45am Devotion 2:00pm Bottle Craft 3:00pm Catholic Mass	**8** 11:30am Exercise 2:00pm Sing-A-Long 6:00pm Movie	**9** 9:00am Coffee Group 6:00pm Movie
10 9:00am Coffee Group 2:00pm Church 6:00pm Old Radio Programs	**11** 9:00am Bedside Act. 11:30am Exercise 2:00pm -(H.S. Wrestlers Perform on Mats) 2:00pm Men's Club 6:00pm Youth Club	**12** 9:00am Coffee & Donuts 10:00am Do You Remember? 11:30am States & Capitals 11:45am Devotions 2:00pm Crafts (Decopague	**13** 9:00am Bedside 11:30am Exercise 11:45am Devotions 2:00pm Bingo 2:00pm Singer	**14** 9:00am Beauty Club 11:30am States & Capital 3:00pm Catholic Mass 3:00pm History Club (Rev War)	**15** 11:30am Exercise 11:45am Tasty Terms 2:00pm Rhythm Band 6:00pm Wine & Cheese	**16** 9:00am Coffee Group 2:00pm Euchre/Checkers 2:00pm Plant Care
17 9:00am Coffee Group 2:00pm Church 3:00pm Ice Cream Sundaes	**18** 9:00am Bedside Act. 11:30am Exercise 2:00pm -Walking to collect Rocks, Discussion 2:00pm Horticulture Club 6:00pm Slide Show	**19** 10:00am Do You Remember? 11:30am President's Quiz 11:45am Devotions 2:00pm Show & Tell 6:00pm Movie	**20** 9:00am Bedside Act 11:30am Exercise 11:45am Devotions 2:00pm Bingo	**21** 9:00am Beauty Club 11:30am Math Quiz 2:45pm Basketball Game (w/College Team) 3:00pm Catholic Mass	**22** 11:30am Split Infinitives 11:45am Devotions 2:00pm Birthday Party	**23** T V Sports (afternoon) 9:00am Coffee Group 6:00pm Checkers & Dominoes
24 9:00am Coffee Group 2:00pm Church 2:00pm Popcorn Party	**25** 9:00am Bedside Act. 11:30am Exercise 1:00pm Sewing Club (Mending) 6:00pm Movie	**26** Picture Talking Day -- All Day 10:00am Do You Remember? 11:30am Old Measurements Quiz 2:00pm Rhythm Band	**27** 9:00am Bedside Act. 11:30am Exercise 2:00pm Dart Games	**28** 9:00am Beauty Club 11:30am Nursery Rhymes 2:00pm Toss Across 3:00pm Catholic Mass	**29** 11:30am Exercise 11:45am Word Games 2:00pm Balloon Volley Ball	**30** 9:00am Coffee Group 2:00pm Euchre 7:00pm Jeopardy & Wheel of Fortune
31 Family Visits 9:00am Coffee Group 2:00pm Church 6:00pm Old Radio						

September

Sunday	Monday	Tuesday	Wednesday	Thursday	Friday	Saturday
	1 9:00am Bedside Act. 11:30am Exercise 2:00pm Men's Club (Model Car SHow) 6:00pm Social HOur	**2** 10:00am Do You Remember? 1:30am Food Quiz 2:00pm Movie 6:00pm Wine & Cheese Party	**3** 9:00am Bedside Act. 11:30am Football 11:45am Devotions 2:00pm Bingo 6:00pm Band	**4** 9:00am Beauty Club 11:30am Old Slogans 2:00pm Rhythm Band 3:00pm Catholic Mass	**5** 11:30am Exercise (to record) 11:45am Devotions 2:00pm Back to School Party (Spelling Bee)	**6** 9:00am Coffee Group 2:00pm Jigsaw Puzzle
7 9:00am Coffee Group 2:00pm Church 2:00pm Afternoon Movie	**8** 9:00am Bedside 11:30am Exercise 11:45am Devotions 2:00pm Bingo 6:00pm Wine & Cheese	**9** 10:00am Do You Remember? (Current Events) 11:45am Devotions 2:00pm Cooking (Granola)	**10** 9:00am Bedside Act. 11:30am Bear Hunt 11:45am Devotions 2:00pm Bingo	**11** 9:00am Beauty Club 11:30am President Quiz 2:00pm Library Club (Library Speaker) 3:00pm Catholic Mass	**12** 11:30am Exercise 11:45am Devotions 1:00pm Decorating 6:30pm Senior Prom (Families Invited)	**13** 9:00am Coffee Group 2:00pm Euchre & Checkers
14 9:00am Coffee Group 2:00pm Church 3:00pm Popcorn Party	**15** 9:00am Bedside Act. 11:30am Exercise 2:00pm Hospitality CLub (Visit Bed Pt.) 6:00pm Movie	**16** 10:00am Do You Remember? 11:30am New York Quiz 11:45am Devotions 2:00pm Resident Council	**17** 9:00am Bedside Act. 11:30am Simon Says 11:45am Devotions 2:00pm Bingo	**18** 9:00am Beauty Club 11:30am Times & Seasons Quiz 2:00pm History Club (WWII Vet) 3:00pm Catholic Mass	**19** 11:45am Exercise 2:00pm Birthday Party 6:00pm Evening Movie	**20** 9:00am Coffee Group 2:00pm Photo Sharing 8:00pm Jeopardy
21 9:00am Coffee Group 2:00pm Church 3:00pm Scrabble & Dominoes	**22** 9:00am Bedside Ac. 11:30am Exercise 2:00pm (Leaf Collecting & Preserving) 2:00pm Horticulture Club 6:00pm Singer	**23** 10:00am Do You Remember? 11:30am States & Capitals 2:00pm Crafts-Leaf Project 7:00pm Social Hour	**24** 9:00am Bedside Act. 11:30am Exercise 11:45am Devotions 2:00pm Bingo	**25** 9:00am Beauty Club 11:30am Holiday Quiz 2:00pm Paper Potluck 3:00pm Catholic Mass	**26** 9:00am Bedside Act. 11:30am Exercise 11:45am Devotions 2:00pm Rhythm Band	**27** 9:00am Coffee Group 2:00pm Plant Care 6:00pm Movie
28 9:00am Coffee Group 2:00pm Church 6:00pm Old Radio Programs	**29** 9:00am Bedside Act 11:30am Exercise 2:00pm Basketball Game w/School Kids	**30**				

Columbus Day

Sunday	Monday	Tuesday	Wednesday	Thursday	Friday	Saturday
	Columbus Day		**1** 9:00am Bedside Act 11:30am Exercise (Football) 11:45am Devotions 2:00pm Bingo	**2** 9:00am Beauty Club 11:30am Word Games 2:00pm Movie & Popcorn 3:00pm Catholic Mass 6:00pm Singer	**3** 9:00am Bedside Act. 11:30am Exercise 11:45am Devotions 2:00pm Basketball Game Against Another Facility	**4** 9:00am Coffee Group 2:00pm Old Radio 6:00pm Jigsaw Puzzles
5 Family Visits 9:00am Coffee Group 2:00pm Church 6:00pm Checkers	**6** 9:00am Bedside Act 11:30am Exercise 3:00pm Horticulture Club (Transplant Mums) 6:00pm Bible Study	**7** Cooking (Making Apple Butter)-ALL DAY! 10:00am Do You Remember? 11:30am Word Games	**8** 9:00am Bedside Act. 11:30am Exercise (Ball on Sheet) 11:45am Devotions 2:00pm Bingo	**9** 9:00am Beauty Club 11:30am Word Games (Times & Seasons) 2:00pm History Club (Visit Memorial) 3:00pm Catholic Mass	**10** 9:00am Bedside Act. 11:30am Exercise 11:45am Devotions 2:00pm Birthday Party & Clown Visit 6:00pm Social Hour	**11** 9:00am Coffee Group 2:00pm Scramble 6:00pm Movie
12 9:00am Coffee Group 2:00pm Church 2:00pm Afternoon Movie	**13** 9:00am Bedside Act. 11:30am Exercise 3:00pm Hospitality Club (Hang door name tags) 6:00pm Movie	**14** 10:00am Do You Remember? 11:30am Sports Quiz 2:00pm Sing-A-Long	**15** 9:00am Bedside Act. 11:30am Exercise 11:45am Devotions 2:00pm Bingo	**16** 9:00am Beauty Club 11:30am Word Games (Infinitives) 2:00pm Pizza Party 3:00pm Catholic Mass	**17** 9:00am Beauty Club 11:30am Word Games (Old Products) 2:00pm Animal Shelter Visit 3:00pm Catholic Mass	**18** 9:00am Coffee Group 2:00pm Plant Care 6:00pm Wheel of Fortune
19 Family Visit 9:00am Coffee Group 2:00pm Church 6:00pm Scramble	**20** 9:00am Bedside Act. 11:30am Exercise 2:00pm Men's Club (Model R.R. Demo) 6:00pm Bible Study	**21** 10:00am Do You Remember? 2:00pm Superstitions	**22** 9:00am Bedside Act. 11:30am Exercise 11:45am Devotions 2:00pm Bingo	**23** 9:00am Beauty Club 11:30am Word Games (Old Products) 2:00pm Animal Shelter Visit 3:00pm Catholic Mass	**24** Planning Time 11:30am Exercise 2:00pm Rhythm Band 6:00pm Checkers	**25** 9:00am Coffee Group 2:00pm Plant Care 6:00pm Music Appreciation
26 9:00am Coffee Group 2:00pm Church 2:00pm Old Radio Shows	**27** 9:00am Bedside Act. 11:30am Exercise 2:00pm Bible Study 3:00pm Sewing Club (Sock Dolls) 6:00pm Boys Club Visit	**28** 10:00am Do You Remember? 11:30am Name Song Titles 6:30pm Fall Festival (Families Invited)	**29** 9:00am Bedside Act. 11:30am Exercise 11:45am Devotions 2:00pm Bingo	**30** 9:00am Beauty Club 11:30am Old Proverbs 2:00pm Horse Racing 3:00pm Catholic Mass	**31** 11:30am Exercise 11:45am Devotions 2:00pm Rhythm Band 6:00pm Euchre	COMMUNION

November

Sunday	Monday	Tuesday	Wednesday	Thursday	Friday	Saturday
						1 9:00am Coffee Group 2:00pm Piano & Sing-A-Long 6:00pm Jigsaw Puzzles
2	**3** 9:00am Bedside Act. 11:30am Exercise 1:00pm Outing to Restaurant 2:00pm Hospitality Club (Address Christmas Cards)	**4** 10:00am Do You Remember? 11:30am Spelling Bee 11:45am Devotions	**5** 9:00am Bedside Act. 11:30am Exercise 11:45am Devotions 2:00pm Bingo	**6** 9:00am Beauty Club 11:30am Word Games 2:00pm Movie & Popcorn 3:00pm Catholic Mass 6:00pm Social Hour	**7** 11:30am Exercise 11:45am Devotions 1:00pm History Club (Civil War Story) 2:00pm Singer 6:00pm Movie	**8** 9:00am Coffee Group 2:00pm Plant Care 6:00pm Movie
9 9:00am Coffee Group 2:00pm Church 6:00pm Movie	**10** 9:00am Bedside Act. 11:30am Exercise 2:00pm Men's Club (Euchre & Checker Tournament) 2:00pm Bible Study 6:00pm Social Hour	**11** 10:00am Do You Remember? 11:45am Word Games 2:00pm Resident Council 6:00pm Juggler	**12** 9:00am Bedside Act. 11:30am Exercise 11:45am Devotions 2:00pm Bingo 6:00pm Old Radio 6:00pm Barber Shop Quartet	**13** 9:00am Beauty Clu 11:30am Famous People Quiz 2:00pm Basketball with School Kids 3:00pm Catholic Mass	**14** 11:45am Devotions 2:00pm Sing-A-Long 6:00pm Slide Show	**15** 9:00am Coffee Group 2:00pm Euchre 6:00pm Old Radio
16 9:00am Coffee Group 2:00pm Church 6:00pm Old Radio	**17** 9:00am Bedside Act. 11:30am Exercise 1:00pm Decorate Christmas Tree 2:00pm Bible Study 3:00pm Sewing Club (Sock Dolls)	**18** 10:00am Do You Remember? 1:30am Word Games 2:00pm Christmas Craft (Placements) 6:00pm Bell Choir	**19** 9:00am Bedside Act. 11:30am Exercise (Simon Says) 11:45am Devotions 2:00pm Bingo	**20** 9:00am Beauty Club 11:30am Word Games 2:00pm Ann Landers 3:00pm Catholic Mass 6:00pm Movie	**21** 11:30am Exercise 11:45am Devotions 2:00pm Sort Christmas Decorations	**22** 9:00am Coffee Group 2:00pm Plant Care 3:00pm Lincoln Log Cabin Contest
23 9:00am Coffee Group 2:00pm Church 6:00pm Choir	**24** 9:00am Bedside Act. 11:30am Exercise 2:00pm Birthday Party	**25** 10:00am Do You Remember? 11:30am Word Games (Old Proverbs) 2:00pm Cooking (Reese Peanut Butter Cups) 6:00pm Family Turkey Dinner	**26** 9:00am Bedside Act. 11:30am Exercise 11:45am Devotions 2:00pm Bingo 6:00pm Wine & Cheese Party	**27** HAPPY THANKSGIVING Thanksgiving Turkey Dinner FAMILY VISITS 6:00pm Movie	**28** 11:45am Devotions 2:00pm Horse Racing	**29**
30 9:00am Coffee Group 2:00pm Church 3:00pm Jigsaw Puzzles 6:00pm Checkers						

Sunday	Monday	Tuesday	Wednesday	Thursday	Friday	Saturday
	1 9:00am Bedside Act. 11:30am Exercise 2:00pm Hospitality Club (Decorate Doors)	**2** Decorate Facility 10:00am Do You Remember? 11:30am Christmas Carols on Tape 2:00pm Bingo	**3** 9:00am Bedside Act. 11:30am Exercise 11:45am Devotions 2:00pm Christmas Movie 6:00pm Carollers	**4** 9:00am Beauty Club 11:30am States & Capitals 3:00pm Catholic Mass 3:00pm Resident Council	**5** 11:30am Exercise 11:45am Devotions 2:00pm Outing: Ride to see City Decorations 6:00pm Church Visit	**6** 9:00am Coffee Group 2:00pm Euchre & Check 6:00pm Old Radio
7 9:00am Coffee Group 2:00pm Church 6:00pm Carollers	**8** 10:00am Do You Remember? 11:30am Word Games (20 Questions) 2:00pm Craft Club (Pill Bottle Tree Ornaments)	**9** 10:00am Do You Remember? 11:30am Exercise 11:45am Devotions 2:00pm Christmas Shopping (In-House, provided by church)	**10** 9:00am Bedside Act. 11:30am Exercise 2:00pm Bingo 2:00pm Nursery School Christmas Play 3:00pm Gift Wrapping for Community	**11** 9:00am Beauty Club 11:30am Devotions 11:45am Jokes & Riddles 2:00pm Basketball Game 3:00pm Catholic Mass	**12** 9:00am Coffee Group 2:00pm Gift Wrapping Service 7:00pm Wheel of Fortune	**13** 9:00am Coffee Group 2:00pm Plant Care 3:00pm Christmas Movie
14 Family Visits 9:00am Coffee Group 2:00pm Church 6:00pm Carollers	**15** 9:00am Bedside Act. 11:30am Exercise 2:00pm (Christmas Music & Cookies) 2:00pm McDonald's Visit 6:00pm Salvation Army	**16** 10:00am Do You Remember? (Christmas Long Ago) 11:45am Devotions 2:00pm Male Paper Chain 6:00pm Movie	**17** 9:00am Bedside Act. 11:30am Exercise 11:45am Devotions 2:00pm Bingo 6:00pm Carollers	**18** Give Away Sock Dolls 9:00am Beauty Club 11:30am Sing-A-Long 3:00pm Catholic Mass 6:00pm Movie	**19** 11:30am Exercise 11:45am Devotions 2:00pm Resident Christmas Party 6:00pm Social Hour	**20** 9:00am Coffee Group 11:30am Read: Visit from St. Nick 3:00pm Christmas Tea
21 9:00am Coffee Group 1:00pm Church Christmas Program 2:00pm Church 6:00pm Carollers	**22** 9:00am Bedside Act. 11:30am Exercise 2:00pm Discussion: My Christmas 5:00pm Penny Pitching	**23** 10:00am Do You Remember? 11:30am Exercise 11:45am Devotions 2:00pm Nursery Rhymes	**24** 9:00am Bedside Act. 11:30am Exercise 11:45am Devotions 2:00pm Bingo 7:00pm Wine & Cheese Party	**25** 'MERRY CHRISTMAS' Christmas Carols on Tape Christmas Dinner Family Visits 2:00pm Church	**26** 9:00am Coffee Group 2:00pm Good-By 1991 Party 6:00pm Movie	**27** 9:00 AM Coffee Group 2:00 PM Bird Feeding & Watching 6:00 PM Movie
28 9:00 AM Coffee Group 2:00 PM Church 6:00 PM Movie	**29** 9:00am Bedside Act. 11:30am Sing-A-Long 1:00pm Men's Club (Speaker: Airplanes) 2:00pm Bible Study 6:00pm Movie	**30** 9:00am Coffee & Newspaper 11:30am Exercise 11:45am Devotions 2:00pm Rhythm Band	**31** 11:30am Exercise 11:45am Devotions 2:00pm Fireman Visit 6:00pm Wine & Cheese Party			

Daily	Weekly	Monthly	Yearly	Occasionally	Seasonally	New Ideas
		Projects	Community Involvement	Fill-ins	Outings	Cooking

Valley Press, P.O. Box 5224, Lafayette, IN 47903

Notes

Notes